Praise for *Deep Tech and the* ⌐

GW00771383

A powerful blueprint for developing a 21st-century purposeful organisation. CEOs, designers and technologists alike will all take inspiration from this transdisciplinary approach to Deep Tech."
— Dave Gray, Founder of XPLANE and author of *The Connected Company,*
   Gamestorming and *Liminal Thinking*

"A future we have never experienced was birthed while many weren't looking. The authors offer a profound shift in perspective in this insightful roadmap for Deep Tech—the possibilities, the unintended consequences and the compelling need to make the human dimension (and truth) a more powerful part of the equation. In your hand is an essential playbook for the future. Drink in the soulful wisdom on these pages. The evolution of humanity depends on it."
— Kimberly Faith, Systems Thinking Expert, Futurist and Award Winning Author

"In a context of continuous change, the connection between platforms, purpose, people and our planet represents a promising path for the challenges of Industry 4.0. Deep Tech and the Amplified Organisation inspires us to promote more collaborative environments in organisations, where creativity and knowledge can be shared to solve present and future challenges, generating a conscious impact for a better world".
— Ricardo Carvalho, CEO of CBA – Companhia Brasileira de Alumínio

Brilliant! *Deep Tech and the Amplified Organisation* provides a path for leaders to action and reflection in uncertain times. Unlike other organisational and technology-oriented frameworks, it underlines the significance of human values and the potential, creativity and profound impact decision-making has on our planet's natural ecosystems. A must read for those stepping into the future, change agents and systems thinkers!
— Andrea Somoza-Norton, Ed.D, Associate Professor, Educational Leadership
   and Administration Program, California Polytechnic State University

"It can be easy at times for those of us working in sustainability to feel pessimistic about the future and the direction that current technology trends are taking us. *Deep Tech and the Amplified Organisation* offers concepts and solutions that leverage deep technology to help us re-engage with our universal human values. This is a fascinating and inspiring read that anyone passionate about technology, sustainability, or the future of humanity will want to read."

— Denise DeLuca, Director, MCAD Sustainable Design Masters program, Board President of the International Society of Sustainability Professionals and author of *Re-Aligning with Nature: Ecological Thinking for Radical Transformation*

"At a time when the adoption of advanced technologies is accelerating, *Deep Tech and the Amplified Organisation* and its authors show how a systemic view and the relationships between these new technologies, humanity and the environment are of fundamental importance, since moments of true evolution never have technology as an end in itself."

— Giuliano Michel Fernandes, Head of Marketing and Communications, CBMM

"In an era reeling from the unintended consequences of shortsighted technological applications, it's refreshing to see a clear-eyed business strategy for reinventing the application of deep technology platforms so that they leverage and amplify social equity and ecological vitality. The authors of *Deep Tech and the Amplified Organisation* lay out a bold blueprint for business leaders to spark a collective and purpose-centred scaling of systemic organisational impact that makes a regenerative future more possible. If we ever have any hope of redirecting deep technologies to holistically serve human aspirations for a better future for all, this book is an impressive contribution to that roadmap."

— Scott Boylston, Graduate Coordinator, SCAD Design for Sustainability Masters Program and author of *Designing with Society*

DEEP TECH

AND THE AMPLIFIED
THE

ORGANISATION

hol
pub

holonomics
publishing

How to elevate, scale and amplify your business through the New 4Ps of platforms, purpose, people and planet

DEEP TECH

AND THE **AMPLIFIED ORGANISATION**

SIMON ROBINSON · IGOR COUTO · MARIA MORAES ROBINSON

First published in 2021 by Holonomics Publishing

Holonomics Publishing is the UK-registered publishing division of Holonomics®.

Office 7, 35-37 Ludgate Hill,
London,
EC4M 7JN
www.holonomics.pub

Holonomics® is a registered trademark in the United Kingdom.

A catalogue record for this book is available from the British Library.
ISBN: 978-0-995-71582-0 (paperback)
ISBN: 978-0-995-71583-7 (ePub)

Because of the dynamic nature of the Internet, any web addresses or links contained in this book may have changed since publication and may no longer be valid.

Front cover design and layout: Igor Postiga

To our friends, families and colleagues who have supported us in the writing of this book

Contents

Figures

Preface

In 1975, two young Australian electronic enthusiasts, Kim Ryrie and Peter Vogel, had a dream to create "the world's greatest synthesiser".[1] Despite starting with just a few hundred dollars, they launched their flagship product in 1979, the Fairlight CMI, the first commercially available synthesiser to include sampling technology, allowing it to reproduce any sound in the world. While no more than 500 were sold over the Fairlight's production history due to it costing USD 100,000 in today's money, the machine revolutionised pop music, starting with Peter Gabriel who Vogel had managed to meet by chance when he first brought the synthesiser to the UK.

The first artist to purchase the instrument was Led Zeppelin's John Paul Jones, who was soon followed by various prominent UK artists such as Rick Wright, Alan Parsons, Thomas Dolby, Nick Taylor and Kate Bush. The synthesiser was also adopted in the US with artists such as Joni Mitchell, Stevie Wonder and Herbie Hancock.[2]

With an orchestral stab as one of its preset sounds, the sampling power of the Fairlight would lead to the Musician's Union in Britain worrying that their members would no longer be necessary for the production of music. This concern did not diminish the enthusiastic manner in which rock and pop stars fully embraced the new technology and the new creative horizons which had opened up for them. Having broken his collarbone and being unable to drum, Stewart Copeland from the Police would use the second generation CMI's sequencing feature to program, leading him to claim that it had "saved him and put him on the map as a composer".[3] By contrast, when drummer Phil Collins released *No Jacket Required*, he wrote, "There is no Fairlight on this Record" on the album's inner sleeve.

The computational power and musical production applications available to bedroom producers today is enormous in comparison to the tools available to artists from the eighties. GarageBand, which comes as standard on Apple's computers, iPads and iPhones, incorporates artificial intelligence into its drum sequencer capabilities, with an interface that categorises different styles based around fictional drummers, who are able to rapidly identify a pattern to fit around musical and vocal tracks which have been recorded live.

We are now entering a promising new era in which people's creative endeavours are being complemented by a new generation of 'deep technology' whose purpose is to solve meaningful problems and achieve conscious impact in the world. Our globally networked digital economy is being driven by radical advances in artificial intelligence (AI), biotechnology, quantum computing, blockchain, automation and robotics. Computers can now harness the power of quantum mechanics, revolutionising their ability to deal with uncertainty, meaning that new real-world problem solving capabilities have become possible.

Warnings of the dangers of technology and its impact on society are of course not new, two of the most notable cinematic contributions being Fritz Lang's *Metropolis* (1927) and Charlie Chaplin's *Modern Times* (1936). Despite being continually alerted to consequences of technological advancement without checks and balances, we have not yet managed to create a fair and just society where people live in dignity, without inequality and on a planet whose ecosystems are flourishing and healthy.

For this reason, we decided to write this book to present a vision of the future in which organisations are able to grow purposefully and consciously through a framework which encompasses the New 4Ps of platforms, purpose, people and planet. Our aim is to provide a blueprint for what we term the *amplified organisation*, one which is able to elevate, scale and amplify high impact strategy, design and digital architectures.

For deep technologies to truly make an impact, we felt that we needed to expand the definition and conception of Deep Tech to help leaders and decision-makers make sense of the major trends shaping organisations and understand the need for a systemic approach to their digital transformation initiatives. So we came together with the mission of writing a transdisciplinary book which integrated our collective expertise in strategy, innovation, platform design, customer and employee experience, agile development, computational sensemaking and human values. The result is a vision of Deep Tech which is multidimensional, based on the four key pillars of deep impact, deep thinking, deep talent and deep collaboration.

Given that the aim of Deep Tech is to solve human and planetary issues, we wanted to provide a conception that reflected its transdisciplinary nature, rather than focusing *only* on the technologies and their investment opportunities. Our goal in this book, therefore, is to expand and build on previous definitions. Our reason for doing so is that many businesses and organisations are failing to reach their full potential by not having a blueprint which integrates their strategy, marketing, design, platforms, digital operations, human resources and data analysis capabilities into a single systemic operating model.

Across our many years of collective experience in helping organisations to transform, we identified a number of interrelated behaviours that act to inhibit the path of growth, the ten most important ones being:

i.   Not taking a systemic approach to strategy, thereby failing to align the organisation through interdependent objectives, indicators, goals and projects;

ii. Placing a disproportionate amount of value on technology in comparison to the people in the organisation who ultimately deliver value;

iii. Design initiatives which do not reach the stage of materialisation to due a lack of integration with strategy;

iv. The core value proposition not being articulated clearly, thereby not being communicated across the organisation, ecosystem and out to clients, customers and wider stakeholders;

v.   A lack of understanding of the logic of platforms and the digital economy which results in millions of dollars wasted in the development of digital systems that fail to integrate into a coherent and scalable enterprise-wide architecture;

vi. Vast quantities of data which are collected but not used due to a lack of deep analytical and computational sensemaking capabilities;

vii. Complex platform architectures which are built and deployed in functional silos, without reference to the enterprise digital operating model;

viii. A lack of necessary talent due to drawing upon a pool of professionals who come from a limited educational sphere;

ix.   A focus on the customer experience at the expense of the employee and developer experience;

x.   A lack of explicit inclusion of human values to provide the foundation of the organisation's culture, quality of relationships and level of leadership consciousness.

This book provides a structured approach to helping organisations overcome these obstacles, thereby enabling them to elevate their value propositions, scale their technologies and platforms and amplify their impact. Its aim is to develop a systemic vision of Deep Tech which is applicable to every aspect of an amplified organisation and every person who plays a part, no matter what their role may be.

The book is divided into three main parts, starting with the first three chapters which explore the concept of deep technology—where the term originated, the size of opportunity and its relevance to ESG obligations (economic, social and governance). We explain how the potential of Deep Tech will only be achieved if it is built on a foundation of systemic thinking, universal human values and deep collaboration, providing examples through the frameworks of living systems theory, strategy mapping and lived experience.

With these foundations in place, we then move to the next three chapters in which we take a deep dive into platform architectures, digital systems and our Deep Tech Discovery design methodology. We explain how an organisation can become amplified and achieve meaningful impact through implementing a systemic approach which aligns and integrates these technologies and practices with an organisation's strategy, digital operating model, digital backbone and elevated value proposition.

Our focus is on developing *platform vision* inside an organisation where every person understands the logic, architecture and rational of a platform's services, growth capabilities and extension points. We have therefore included a comprehensive set of figures and schematics which reveal the often hidden or little-understood qualities of platform architectures, bringing together architectural principles, application design, service interactions and digital operation models into an integrated digital infrastructure, and showing how they relate to the platform lifecycle, design conventions and data analytics necessary for organisations to reach scale and achieve their purpose.

We conclude this part by explaining the key drivers of Deep Tech—technology with soul, purpose-centred design, augmented agility and networked intelligence.

These drivers combine to help an organisation elevate its value and amplify its impact through the deepest form of collaboration between people and machines, thereby reaching a new level of integration of computational sensemaking and human knowledge.

Our framing of Deep Tech within the New 4Ps of platforms, purpose, people and planet focuses on the way in which technology can be of service to people and help organisations reach higher ground through innovation developed with values and consciousness. The final part of the book therefore returns to the core of Deep Tech—the human dimension—explaining how a lack of diversity and inclusion can be overcome through the model of social impact as a service, the employee experience and the process of self-knowledge. We explain how both our conception of leadership and the practice of design thinking can evolve through a shift to collective mastery, demonstrating how organisations can articulate their purpose, essence and soul through the Holonomic Circle, a framework which takes an organisation into the human values, lived experiences and quality of relationships of both external clients and internal employees.

Throughout the book we discuss the profound shift in the relationship between people and technology. We have now reached a stage where we are no longer able to distinguish whether written texts, works of art, music and videos have been produced by people or by applications powered by AI. To demonstrate the advanced stage of technology and the high level of intelligence that computers now have, we have provided executive summaries of each chapter which were written not by ourselves, but by GPT-3, the world's most powerful artificial intelligence language generator (at the time of writing), developed by the research laboratory OpenAI.

GPT-3 developed its abilities by absorbing the majority of writing from the entire internet. This vast amount of data was then processed using deep learning analytics to produce a system capable of both summarising existing texts and also producing new ones based on human prompting. You will see examples at the end of each chapter, which are GPT-3's summaries based on our request for it to be relatively creative in its approach and not sticking too closely to the key words, phrases and concepts detected. Having produced a number of paragraphs summarising each chapter section, we selected the most interesting and applied a very light form of editing, taking out repetitive words and altering the grammar (but not meaning) to fit in with our singular narrative voice.

We found one summary that GPT-3 produced as particularly impressive:

"Deep Tech is the soul of technology. It's about using technology to solve our deepest challenges to bring the new into being and create transformation that matters."

One particularly noteworthy aspect of the quality of writing of GPT-3 is that the phrases and texts produced are not copied from other authors. This level of ability is now currently being deployed in over 300 applications such as Viable, which identifies themes, emotions and feelings from customer feedback; Fable Studios, who are creating a new genre of interactive stories through 'virtual beings'; and Algolia, which provides semantic searches through natural language queries.[4]

Given the computational power we have available today at a small fraction of the cost of the technologies of the 1980s, we now need to raise our consciousness and responsibility for its use. For this reason, underlying all aspects of Deep Tech—the technology, architectures, applications and business models—lie the universal human values of peace, truth, love, righteousness and non-violence and the New 4Ps of platforms, purpose, people and planet. It is only when these human values are truly lived that we can design platforms and deep technologies with elevated value propositions that serve to scale and amplify their impact on society and the regeneration of our planet's natural ecosystems.

We close this book by providing a visual and systemic blueprint of the amplified organisation. This has been created to help leaders, decision-makers, entrepreneurs, technologists and designers implement those actions necessary to elevate their organisations and amplify their impact in the world. The blueprint shifts people from a mechanistic way of conceiving their organisations to a living systems understanding, empowering them to realise their full potential through the quality of their relationships and their continual ability to evolve in response to changes in their circumstances and environment.

The opportunity for regeneration through digital ecosystems is immense. We hope you join us on this journey, collectively designing and implementing the next generation of Deep Tech, designed with conscious purpose and where people and amplified organisations can truly flourish and thrive.

São Paulo, Brazil
27th July, 2021

1

CHAPTER ONE

Why
Deep Tech?

THE CASE FOR DEEP TECH

"The power of the web to transform people's lives, enrich society and reduce inequality is one of the defining opportunities of our time."[5] These are the words of British computer scientist Sir Tim Berners-Lee, inventor of the world wide web which he created in 1989, and which launched commercially in 1992. A decade earlier in 1984, Apple had realised its vision of creating a home computer for the "bemused, confused and intimidated" as their first Mac advert declared.[6] With computers now becoming easy to use for anyone, and with an exponential explosion of open access to websites, libraries, businesses, research institutions and any other organisation wishing to make information freely available, our world as we knew it transformed into a new digital reality.

While Apple's mission was to help people fully exploit their creativity, it would be the world wide web which would completely transform the way we used computers and which would subsequently revolutionise the way in businesses operated in the 1990s. With growing numbers of people becoming connected to the internet at home and work, and with a new generation of mobile devices such as Personal Digital Assistants, this decade unleashed an entirely new form of startup characterised by their disruptive business models based on platform architectures and ignited by their founders' passion and desire to achieve incredible rates of growth. The ultimate aim of investors was to achieve their exit goals through lucrative initial public offerings.

While many startups burned through their funds with little sign of achieving profitability, the human cost of those ventures that failed was high, with many Silicon Valley workers suffering burn out from alcoholism, insomnia, mental breakdowns and physical illness.[7] From this period only a handful of startups survive today. This is not surprising given the logic of the angels and venture capitalists behind their creation, investing in many in the hope that just a handful would survive to become unicorns—startups reaching a market capitalisation of USD 1 billion or more.

The most famous of course is Amazon, founded by an ambitious Jeff Bezos in 1994, who immediately saw the commercial potential of online business. The company began trading in 1995 selling books online. In September 2018 Amazon had reached an intraday market valuation of USD 1 trillion, just one month after Apple had become the first company to achieve this milestone, making it one of the world's top one hundred most valuable brands.[8]

But while Amazon prospered, billions of dollars of investment was pouring into many more startups which burned through their funds at breathtaking rates, never managing to become viable long-term enterprises. One of the most well-publicised casualties of this era was Boo.com, a European fashion retailer founded in 1998 with global ambitions to become "the world-leading internet-based retailer of prestigious brand leisure and sportswear names".[9] In their desire to replicate the physical clothes-buying experience as closely as possible, their monthly costs of cataloguing and photographing each item of stock reached USD 500,000.[10]

With most home-internet connections not yet on broadband, it was an idea too advanced for the technology available at the time, resulting in web pages which were clunky and far too slow to load up. Believing that first mover advantage was everything for a global internet brand, USD 130 million was invested in Boo.com. But with bills for staff, technology and marketing spiralling fast, the company closed on the 18th of May 2000, when no further funding was raised.

The first dot-com bubble had truly burst but the dreams of many young entrepreneurs were still alive. The internet became faster, broadband became available, mobile phone usage exploded and the first web-enabled smart phones were introduced. We started to stream music, watch videos and share photos. Our mobile phones became so powerful that they began to replace many other gadgets and items such as diaries, radios, CD players, cam corders, calculators, torches and alarm clocks. And then technology became social. This was Web 2.0.

Berners-Lee's original vision for the web was as "a collaborative medium, a place where we could all meet and read and write".[11] Web 2.0 did not represent new technologies as such, it was more a term to describe the participatory and social nature of the way in which we were using the internet. His original vision was now starting to become reality, with static web pages transforming through user-generated activity such as account registration, liking, tagging, blogging and uploading and sharing videos.[12]

Social networks brought us together on a massive scale, and as we spent more of our working and leisure time online, businesses became more virtual. But then what happened next? And at what cost? As Tom Goodwin famously remarked: "Uber, the world's largest taxi company, owns no vehicles. Facebook, the world's most popular media owner, creates no content. Alibaba, the most valuable retailer, has no inventory. And Airbnb, the world's largest accommodation provider, owns no real estate. Something interesting is happening".

Something interesting was indeed happening—unforeseen and detrimental social, economic and environmental impacts—consequences of the new digital business paradigm which Goodwin's viral phrase had not captured. In June 2021, for example, an undercover investigation by ITV revealed that Amazon was routinely destroying millions of items of unsold stock from one of their UK fulfilment centres each year. Products such as "smart TVs, laptops, drones, hairdryers, top of the range headphones, computer drives, books galore", and, as one ex-employee revealed, "Dyson fans, Hoovers, the occasional MacBook and iPad; and 20,000 Covid (face) masks still in their wrappers" were all routinely marked to be destroyed.[13] An ITV film crew tracked lorries carrying large bins of waste which were then "dumped at either recycling centres or, worse, a landfill site".[14] The cause of this destruction is due to Amazon's business model for which it is cheaper to destroy items rather than continue to maintain them in warehouses after a certain amount of time.

While some commentators framed the new business models as being part of the nascent 'sharing economy', supposedly both sustainable and empowering, it was also possible to view the same practices as being central to a competitive and unprincipled 'gig economy'—a form of capitalism based on the exploitation of the many for the benefit of the few, with people losing all of their traditional safety nets and benefits such as holiday leave, overtime pay, unemployment assistance and healthcare.

While Goodwin highlighted an entirely new logic for the operation of these new platform-based businesses, his often-cited quote did not address the many scandals, sharp business practices and the human cost behind many of the world's biggest startup success stories. We can look at Facebook as one of the defining examples. We as users are not Facebook's principle customers, the data we produce is the inventory it sells. Data exploitation behind Facebook's business model became abundantly clear to its millions of uses when in 2018, Christopher Wylie, a whistleblower from British company Cambridge Analytica, revealed how he had worked together with a Cambridge University academic to amass, extract and exploit private data from 50 million individuals, with the aim of profiling them and then targeting them with political advertisements.

As Wylie revealed to the Observer, Cambridge Analytica exploited Facebook in order to harvest millions of people's profiles. Data from this harvesting was then used to build models to exploit what was known about them and to "target their inner demons".[15] This dysfunctional and dystopian view of social networks is now well and truly mainstream, with, for example, the 2020 American docudrama *The Social Dilemma* revealing the extent of the use and abuse of our personal data. This warning is not new. In 2009, when The Liberal Democrats in the UK proposed the Freedom Bill to counteract restrictions of people's fundamental rights and freedoms, Chris Huhne, Liberal Democrat Home Affairs Spokesman, reminded us that "Orwell's nightmarish 1984 was a warning, not an instruction manual".[16]

Our technology can only ever be as advanced as the collective values we live by in society. It is not the technology that defines how advanced it is, but the values which inform how we put it to use. For this reason, thirty years after its launch, Tim Berners-Lee called for "governments, companies and citizens from across the world to take action to protect the web as a force for good".[17] *Contract for the Web* was launched as a new initiative to bring experts and citizens with a diverse range of experiences and perspectives together to "build a global plan of action to make our online world safe and empowering for everyone".[18] As Sir Tim explained, "If we don't act now—and act together—to prevent the web being misused by those who want to exploit, divide and undermine, we are at risk of squandering that potential".[19]

We believe in the power of technology to help us achieve our human potential. But we do not believe that technology alone will be our salvation. We need to expand our levels of consciousness, deepen our thinking, discover new avenues of creativity and live our values as authentically as possible. We need to make the shift from advanced technology to deep technology. In short, what we need is technology with soul.

Deep Tech is about using technology to solve our deepest challenges to bring the new into being and create transformation that matters. We believe that Deep Tech is the heart of technology. It represents the soul, the emotion, the striving, the visionary dreams and the yearnings to better society and regenerate our planet.

The days of the lone inventor are over. The global Covid crisis impacted on every single organisation, business and institution in the world, creating a wake-up call like no other. Organisations can no longer rely on the traditional marketing mix of the 4Ps of product, price, place and promotion. The 4Ps, of course, still function for the marketing of products and services, but if organisations wish to implement transformational initiatives, they need the New 4Ps of platforms, purpose, people and planet. Our aim for this book therefore is to help people understand how to create transformation that matters and implement Deep Tech solutions by uniting advanced technological innovations with consciousness and human values.

THE RISE OF THE PLATFORM

In 2015 we coined the phrase *The New 4Ps,* signifying platforms, purpose, people and planet, to highlight to leaders the way in which the new entrepreneurial landscape was changing.[20] While the original 4Ps of product, price, place and promotion were still valid for marketing, they were no longer able to fully frame this new reality and its emerging platform paradigm. Platforms have radically disrupted entire industries, changed consumer and business consumption behaviours and led to radical new ways for enterprises to create value. The result is that six of the world's ten most valuable companies now have platform-based business models worth approximately $13.7 trillion in market value (July 2021).[21]

Many different signs point towards their continual growth and higher concentration of wealth and assets, with few other organisations currently prepared or able to compete at this global level. While companies like Apple, Google, Amazon and Alibaba have been relentless in their pursuit of hyper-connected platform-based paradigms to grow exponentially and win significant market share from more traditional businesses, 92% of executives believe their current business models are not economically viable in a digital economy.[22]

TABLE 1.1 The Global Top 10 Companies by Market Capitalisation (July 2021)

Rank	Company name	Location	Sector	Market Capitalisation (USD)
1	Apple	United States	Technology	2.456 T
2	Microsoft Corp	United States	Technology	2.124 T
3	Amazon.com	United States	Consumer Services	1.893 T
4	Saudi Aramco	Saudi Arabia	Oil and Gas	1.852 T
5	Alphabet (Google)	United States	Technology	1.740 T
6	Facebook	United States	Technology	1.005 T
7	Tenecent	Mainland China	Technology	684 B
8	Tesla	United States	Technology	656 B
9	TSMC	Taiwan	Technology	650 B
10	Berkshire Hathaway	United States	Financials	638 B

Market capitalisation is just one way to rank companies. In addition to looking at earnings or revenue, it is also possible to create alternative rankings using a composite score based on sales, profits, assets and market value, etc. When measuring the world's largest public companies from these different perspectives, the central power of banks and the rise of China come into view, together with more traditional companies such as Walmart, Volkswagen and Samsung.[23] The concentration of power is not just financial wealth and technology but geographical and political in nature. Platforms are now impacting significantly on the nature of employment and the way in which personal data is utilised. For this reason, we need to explore and understand what it means to be human in such an advanced technological world and the impact human behaviour is having on nature's ecosystems.

The seismic changes from both advances in technology and the global Covid health crisis resulted in the world's billionaire's wealth increasing by more than a quarter (27.5%) from April to July 2020. According to Swiss bank UBS, there were 2,189 billionaires in 2020. Total billionaire wealth reached USD 10.2 trillion at the end of July 2020, surpassing the previous peak of USD 8.9 trillion, reached at the end of 2017.[24] Between 2018 and the first seven months of 2020, entrepreneurs in the tech, healthcare and industrial sectors saw the greatest gains. Geographically, by early April 2020, there were 389 Chinese billionaires, worth a total of USD 1.2 trillion. Their wealth had grown by almost nine times, compared with twice in the US.[25]

As the United Nations recognised in their *Digital Economy Report*, digital and more specifically platform technologies have the ability to contribute to the UN Sustainable Development Goals while also potentially hampering their progress.[26] The reason is that if no actions are taken, the barriers to entry into platform-based value chains will continue to increase, thereby widening the already existing gap between under-connected and hyper-digitalised countries. As the report cautions, "In the data-driven economy, the companies controlling the data value chains stand the best chance of becoming the lead firms also in sectoral value chains".

With great power comes great responsibility. For this reason, it is interesting to perceive an increase in awareness in billionaires relating to our interrelated and systemic challenges. As USB observed in their research, billionaires are giving more than at any time in history.[27] Philanthropy is of course not new, with donations to educational, scientific, cultural and other causes flourishing in the second industrial revolution in the United States, when many fortunes from the richest families supported and funded schools, universities, libraries and research centres. And now it seems, billionaires may be becoming philanthropists much earlier in their careers, placing their focus on helping to tackle social and environmental problems.[28]

Many entrepreneurs, investors, governments and educational institutions are now waking up to the fact that whereas the previous thirty years have been about mastering code written in 1s and 0s, the next revolution is going to be in the code of life itself.[29] Technologies such as biofuels, biochemicals, rapid gene sequencing and storage of information in bacteria are growing quickly. We have reached the stage whereby scientists can use human cells to make embryonic stem cells. This means that it is now possible to take skin, stomach and bone cells, program new stem cells, and turn these stem cells into a full organ. We are learning how to create genetically modified human beings.[30]

The implication of these developments is that the digital revolution of the last thirty years could well be seen as tiny compared to the much greater wave of the life sciences revolution. As researcher, entrepreneur and venture capitalist Juan Enríquez, one of the world's leading authorities on the economic and political impacts of life sciences puts it: "Wealth derives from code. Life code will probably become the single biggest driver of the global economy in the future. Those countries who are wealthy are the ones who have access to, and understand code. Not just computer code, but the code of life itself".[31]

Companies such as Dupont, BASF, Toyota and GE are all transforming their businesses via the opportunities which these developments in life sciences are bringing. As Werner Baumann, CEO of Bayer explains, companies such as his have the power to enact global transformations:

> "There is a broad consensus that the way we live and manage our economy is not sustainable. We face an urgent call to action. A large share of that responsibility lies with industrial companies like Bayer because with our size and strength we are capable of making a difference. In light of Covid, we can clearly see that we need to think bigger to succeed with the transformation to a sustainable economy. We need new technologies, breakthrough innovation and sustainable business models."[32]

With headquarters in Leverkusen, Germany, Bayer AG is one of the world's largest multinational pharmaceutical and life sciences company. In 2018 Bayer acquired Monsanto, and with it a number of major litigation processes, resulting in the company agreeing to spend more than USD 12 billion to resolve thousands of US lawsuits and deal with future claims.[33] While taking into account the reputational issues relating to Bayer's historical actions, it is still interesting to see how the company is investing in early-stage funding projects, a strategy which in their words allows "companies to focus on the long-term delivery of their disruptive technology, rather than short-term and lower impact results".[34]

This investment in the health and agricultural sectors is done through their impact investment arm, Leaps by Bayer. This name reflects the following the ten major challenges they have identified which humanity now faces:

i.   Cure genetic diseases
ii. Provide sustainable organ replacement
iii. Reduce the environmental impact of agriculture
iv. Prevent and cure cancer
v.   Regenerate lost tissue function
vi. Reverse autoimmune diseases
vii. Cure through microbiome health
viii. Develop sustainable protein supplies
ix. Eradicate insect-borne infections
x.   Drive transformational digital business models[35]

The most advanced technologies being developed today are breaking previous limits on lifespan, health and cognition. At the same time, many different risks are now converging, presenting the possibility of major existential and catastrophic risks to humans, including ethics and identity, ecosystem degradation and loss of biodiversity, social and technological exclusion, climate change, food insecurity and fresh water availability, scarcity of rare metals and other vital natural resources, and unregulated powerful new technologies. So while on the one hand humanity is facing these huge challenges, there are many investors, entrepreneurs and organisations who have set their sights on finding creative solutions to these problems, understanding that purely focusing on shareholder value is no longer sufficient as a business goal in the twenty-first century.

A review of over 200 sources on environmental, social, and governance (ESG) performance by Oxford University and Arabesque showed that in the overwhelming majority of companies that focused on sustainability, "operational performance was improved, translating to higher cash flows".[36] For this reason, many organisations are now placing considerable emphasis on their ESG obligations which relate to an organisation's operations that socially conscious investors examine when evaluating potential investments. Recognising that the integration of ESG criteria into an organisational strategy can be financially beneficial, sustainable investing and reporting are now mainstream business activities.

Our Deep Tech approach does not separate or distinguish sustainability from regeneration, which at times can be perceived as conceptually different practices. We start with sustainability as the 'why' of an organisation's future vision, the central concept pertaining to the ability to continue over a long of time in a manner that does not harm the environment. Regeneration is therefore the 'what', in that it relates to actions and initiatives that improve a place or system, allowing them to recover from damage and become strong and successful again.

ESG strategy can therefore be understood as the need for organisations to ensure that their operations sustain life on earth through the adoption of regenerative operations and business practices. The way in which this can be put into practice, the 'how', will be different for each organisation and their wider social, economic and ecological context.

To emphasise just how important ESG criteria now are, in September 2020, research from the Swiss Re Institute showed that a fifth of countries worldwide are at risk from ecosystem collapse as biodiversity declines.[37] In order to reach this conclusion, Swiss Re created a new index which combines biodiversity and ecosystem indicators to help insurers assess ecosystem risks when setting premiums for businesses. According to Jeffrey Bohn, Swiss Re's chief research officer, the index could have a wider use as it "allows businesses and governments to factor biodiversity and ecosystems into their economic decision-making".[38]

Our Deep Tech ecosystem is now exploring 'deep challenges', a term we use to refer to those systemic global problems in which human, technological, digital, biological and ecological factors are intractably interwoven. Technology alone is not a solution. We cannot therefore create the fourth industrial revolution with the same level of consciousness which built the previous three. We need an expanded form of consciousness and the practice of human values. In short, we need to rethink technology. We need to put a beating heart into technology and reanimate its soul. We need to make the shift from a scarcity mindset into a Deep Tech people and planet mindset. This shift is summarised in Table 1.2.

TABLE 1.2 The Qualities of a Deep Tech Mindset

Scarcity mindset	People and planet mindset
unethical	values
wasteful	regenerative
controlling/manipulative	empowering/liberating
centralised power	democratic
counterfeit	authentic
secret	transparent
quantitative exponential growth	qualitative meaningful growth

DEFINING DEEP TECH

The term 'Deep Tech' was coined by Swati Chaturvedi, CEO of investment firm Propel(x), which was founded in 2013 with the mission of facilitating private venture capital for startups in the life sciences, energy, clean technology, computer sciences, materials and chemicals sectors. Propel(x) decided to use the term 'Deep Tech' as a way to define a new category of startup. Writing in 2014, Chaturvedi explained that:

"Deep technology companies are built on tangible scientific discoveries or engineering innovations. They are trying to solve big issues that really affect the world around them. For example, a new medical device or technique fighting cancer, data analytics to help farmers grow more food, or a clean energy solution trying to lessen the human impact on climate change."[39]

This conception allows Propel(x) to differentiate Deep Tech startups from those startups innovating through new business models based on existing technologies. From this perspective therefore, deep technology startups have the defining characteristics of i) the ability to disrupt several markets to create considerable economic value for early investors, and ii) a lasting effect on humanity in positive and meaningful ways.[40]

With rapid advances in technological breakthroughs and developments, the phrase 'Deep Tech' has also been used to focus on categories of technology. An example comes from TechWorks, a British industrial association which frames Deep Tech in the following manner:

"Deep Tech is often set apart by its profound enabling power, the differentiation it can create and its potential to catalyse change. Deep Tech companies often possess fundamental and defensible engineering innovations that distinguish them from those companies that are focused on the incremental refinement or delivery of standardised technologies or only use business model innovation to create opportunities. Deep Tech can span across many technological areas and can impact diverse applications. On the technological front, these can include processing and computing architecture innovations, advances in semiconductors and electronic systems, power electronics, vision and speech algorithms and techniques, artificial intelligence and machine learning, haptics and more."[41]

A second example of this technology-focused definition comes from TechCrunch, who define Deep Tech as "a generic term for technologies not focused on end-user services that includes artificial intelligence, robotics, blockchain, advanced material science, photonics and electronics, biotech and quantum computing".[42] A related term which has at times been used in place of Deep Tech is 'hard tech'. There is no singular meaning of hard tech, with definitions referring to the category of startup, the complexity of the innovation and the 'hard work' needed due to the difficulty of challenges that these technologies are attempting to solve. With many differing interpretations, we saw an opportunity to expand on previous conceptions of Deep Tech by providing a new conception that explicitly recognises its multidimensional nature.

When 1STi, Holonomics and Vai na Web came together in 2017 to develop our own ecosystem, the Deep Tech Network, we rapidly came to the conclusion that what was emerging was a new perspective on Deep Tech which united our core complementary skills of platform development, digital and cultural transformation, agile strategy and customer experience design. We intuitively felt the need to find a way to refer to all that we felt was missing in existing ways of describing advances in technology and the digital economy. What was missing was a conversation that would include human values, consciousness, artistic investigations, philosophical creativity and the voice of those communities often missing from the monocultural norms of Silicon Valley and the world's great financial and technology centres.

In a nutshell, what was missing was *soul*. Over many conversations and reflections we came to conceive of Deep Tech across multiple dimensions and perspectives, the three principle ones being:

• machinery and equipment developed from the principles described in the Deep Tech manifesto;
• the integration of scientific knowledge, technical design, computational architecture and philosophical creativity;
• the union of advanced technological development with the evolution of human consciousness.

This then allowed us to arrive at our human-centred definition:

Deep Tech is the development of advanced technologies built from a foundation of universal human values by conscious ecosystems.

We use the term 'Deep Tech' not just as a way to define, classify or categorise technologies and industrial sectors, but as a way to live by. Given that our technological solutions can only be as impactful as the level of consciousness and values which created them, we decided to write a Deep Tech manifesto to help people determine if their solutions truly are Deep Tech, and more importantly, to help people understand if their very way of being is Deep Tech.

The Deep Tech Manifesto

i.   The purpose of Deep Tech is to use deep thinking to find profound solutions to complex problems;

ii. Deep Tech combines analytical thinking and artistic consciousness;

iii. Deep Tech creates augmented intelligence—the combination of artificial intelligence with conscious human endeavour;

iv. Privacy and ethics are core elements of Deep Tech algorithms;

v.   Deep Tech is developed by talented people who come from a rich diversity of backgrounds;

vi. The values of Deep Tech are the five universal human values of peace, truth, love, righteousness and non-violence;

vii. Deep Tech helps us to explore our world and ourselves in ever more meaningful ways, honouring what it is to be human in our world.

Our Deep Tech Network is far more than just an ecosystem of organisations. The power, creativity and life of our network is the result of the systemic interplay between four key pillars (Figure 1.1).

FIGURE 1.1 The Four Pillars of Deep Tech

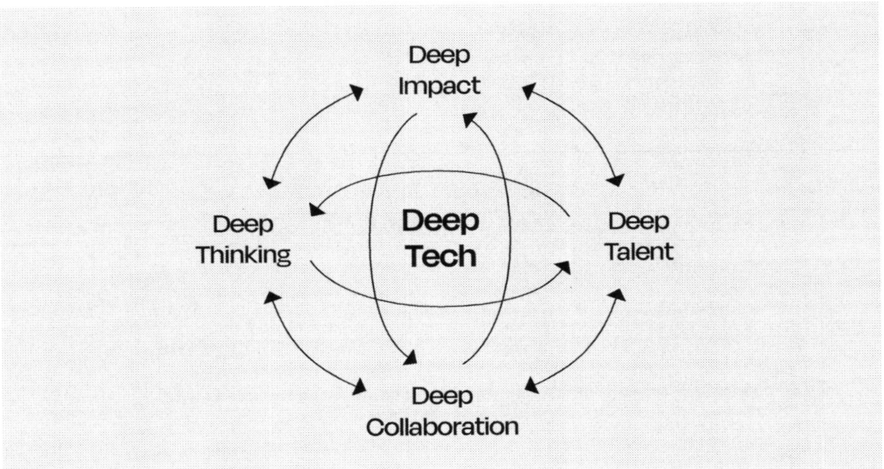

Deep Impact

Deep Impact solutions are based on our Deep Thinking approach to understanding systemic solutions to our complex problems, resulting in the creation of Deep

Tech initiatives, products, services, platforms and architectures. Deep Impact is able to meet the deep challenges of people who are often in vulnerable conditions due to the way it incorporates Deep Talent; people who may not come from traditional academic backgrounds but who are able to empathise and envision real working solutions for different populations. It is based on co-operation, always developing new platforms for collaboration.

Deep Thinking

Deep Thinking provides the philosophical foundations behind all of our initiatives—the ethics, ways of seeing, architectures, creativity and systemic approaches. Deep Thinking contributes to the academic development and teaching of deeply talented people, providing insights into our human condition, psychology and values which allows us to build better tools and platforms for collaboration.

Deep Talent

Deep Talent solves the problem of the skills shortage by empowering and educating people to design and build Deep Tech solutions and initiatives. Deep Talent contributes to Deep Thinking by continually providing different perspectives and framings of challenges, thereby finding solutions that meet many different people's needs, and not just a small segment of society. This pillar teaches us new ways to collaborate, providing new voices and different windows on the world, in order to be able to create systemic solutions to our challenges.

Deep Collaboration

Deep Impact solutions are built using Deep Collaboration platforms which enable large-scale agile ideation, design and implementation tools. Deep Collaboration platforms enable Deep Thinking to be shared and scaled in a manner which is accessible, democratic and impactful. Deep Collaboration tools are accessible to everyone, meaning that people from any background can fully participate and contribute to the movement.

Deep Tech is a way of being which has implications for every aspect of an organisation. We are now experiencing a new industrial revolution where purpose renders our experience of products and services as meaningful; platforms extend our reach into any place; people are the promoters of those brands which make a difference to their lives; and where planetary damage is no longer a price we are willing to pay. For this reason we can no longer think of an organisation's goals in relation to unqualified exponential growth. Organisations in the digital economy will grow through the elevation of their core value propositions, scaling through the power of Deep Tech platforms and the amplification of meaningful solutions. In the following chapters will shall explain in detail exactly how this can be achieved.

Executive Summary

→ The internet has changed the way we work, play and live. It has transformed the way we communicate, shop, bank, travel, entertain ourselves and much more, creating a new digital reality. But what has it cost us? And what will the future hold?

→ The speed of innovation is accelerating ceaselessly through the convergence of breakthrough advances in genomics, computing, artificial intelligence, robotics, synthetic biology, nanotechnology, synthetic chemistry, materials and countless other advanced technologies.

→ Deep Tech is a mindset and a set of values. It is a new way of thinking about the future of technology, business and the world, based on the idea that technology can be used to solve the world's most pressing problems, and that the best way to do this is to create meaningful products and services.

→ We believe that Deep Tech is the heart of technology. It represents the soul, the emotion, the striving, the visionary dreams and the yearnings to better society and regenerate our planet. It is a new way of being which has implications for every aspect of an organisation. It is based on Deep Impact, Deep Thinking, Deep Talent and Deep Collaboration.

→ Deep Tech is not a specific sector or a specific type of technology. It is an orientation to use technology for good and to help us explore our world and ourselves in ever more meaningful ways, honouring what it is to be human in our world.

2

The New 4Ps

DEEP TECH AND THE DIGITAL ECONOMY

The continuing concentration of wealth and technological power raises many important questions as to how we now see the evolution of advanced technology in relation to evolving to more equitable societies and restoring our planet's depleted natural ecosystems. What does it mean to be human in this new reality which is emerging and how will organisations and businesses evolve to ensure that they continue to be meaningful and impactful in our lives? And what shape and form will our economic systems have to make this vision of the future a reality?

The twentieth century gave us high speed innovation in new technological systems. In just seventy years we went from the first manned aircraft to a global network of jet air travel. We went from Alan Turing's code breaking computer of 1945 to Windows 95 in only five decades. It took thirteen years and 2.7 billion dollars to decode the human genome; three decades later you can learn the code of your life in two days for just two hundred dollars.[43]

Our western economic systems have evolved in a manner which rewards those private enterprises which take new technologies and build them into new systems faster and more efficiently than their competitors. But those technologies and systems which are built fast are not necessarily designed to be strong. The twentieth century trained business to build fast. We looked for short term returns over long term gains and learned to prioritise efficiency over resilience.

One example is the way in which artificial intelligence-based systems are developed. As Josh Lovejoy, Head of Design and Ethics at Microsoft, stated in his quest to create AI with purpose: "For an industry that prides itself on moving fast, the tech community has been remarkably slow to adapt to the differences of designing with AI. Machine learning is an intrinsically fuzzy science, yet when it inevitably returns unpredictable results, we tend to react like it's a puzzle to be solved, believing that with enough algorithmic brilliance, we can eventually fit all the pieces into place and render something approaching objective truth. But objectivity and truth are often far afield from the true promise of AI."[44]

We believe that Deep Tech ecosystems have the power to bring business leaders, political leaders, scientists and technologists together to discover ways to make the systems of the world stronger, more resilient and regenerative. While on the one hand caution is required when any technology is allowed to grow exponentially due to the potential of unintended consequences, on the other hand we need to be able to find a way to nurture that growth which benefits humanity and the planet. As we develop an ever deeper understanding of the systems of the world, to build stronger systems we must first learn to see the whole system.

Our purpose in writing this book is to help people think more profoundly about Deep Tech in order to be able to envision strong new systems for the world and amplify those which best serve life on our planet. Advanced technology brings us great benefits and also potential abuses of power, and so for this reason our aim is to inspire meaningful conversations around Deep Tech which are able to contemplate these often contradictory qualities which pioneering leaders can often struggle with. One example is that of Twitter founder Jack Dorsey who explained in 2016 how his feelings about Donald Trump's use of social media were "complicated".[45]

In an interview with The Guardian, Dorsey had spoken about the way in which Trump had "excelled" in his use of this short-form social media commentary. However, Twitter itself would then take a pivotal role at the start of 2021 by being the first social media platform to ban Trump for life. Following the riots at Capital Hill in January 2021, which saw supporters of Trump occupying, vandalising and ransacking parts of the building for several hours, Twitter permanently suspended his account due to "the risk of further incitement of violence".[46]

There are currently no legislative agreements in place as to how to deal with the ethical question of freedom of speech versus the reduction of the spread of hate speech and thereby acts of violence in society. Mitchell Baker has provided a potential framework to answer the question of when to deplatform a head of state, asking "when should platforms make these decisions and is that decision-making power theirs alone?"[47] Pointing out that Trump was clearly not the first politician to exploit the architecture of the internet in this way, she suggested that while silencing or permanently removing bad actors from social media platforms were temporary measures, the following actions could be taken straight away:

- Reveal who is paying for advertisements, how much they are paying and who is being targeted;
- Commit to meaningful transparency of platform algorithms so we know how and what content is being amplified, to whom, and the associated impact;
- Turn on by default the tools to amplify factual voices over disinformation;
- Work with independent researchers to facilitate in-depth studies of the platforms' impact on people and our societies, and what we can do to improve things.[48]

Our global problems are systemic and complex, meaning that we need to find solutions through authentic collaboration and technology ecosystems. To be really able to implement transformational initiatives, both public organisations and privately owned enterprises need new frameworks to help explain how the entrepreneurial reality is changing and thereby help expand their traditional mindsets and ways of thinking.

Business as usual is now no longer an option. For this reason, in 2015 Holonomics created the New 4Ps of Platforms, Purpose, People and Planet—a digital and cultural transformation framework for organisations to utilise prior to any design, strategy and marketing initiatives. When the New 4Ps are integrated into the heart of an organisation, from the start of the strategic planning process through to execution and operation, leaders are better able to develop more agile organisations, improve their employee and customer experience and deliver enhanced value propositions.

I) Platforms

With ever more people becoming connected to the internet at home and work, the new digital economy has unleashed an entirely new form of startup, characterised by new business models based on the logic of platform architectures. Platforms have now disrupted entire industries, changed consumer and business consumption behaviours and created innovative new ways for enterprises to create value. The result as we saw in chapter one is the degree to which platform-based business models are now predominant in six of the world's ten most valuable companies.

II. Purpose

The New 4Ps framework provides a new perspective on customer and employee experience design by helping leaders fully integrate their purpose with their strategies and their customer experience. This is done in an authentic manner by implementing human values across the whole organisation and developing long-term and more meaningful relationships with their customers, stakeholders and the human and environmental ecosystems in which they operate. As Sarah Rozenthuler, author of *Powered by Purpose* puts it, "The living of a real purpose puts fire in our belly, a glow in our hearts and light in our eyes".[49]

III. People

Combined advances in both technology and the life sciences together mean that we are now entering the fourth industrial revolution, one in which our physical, digital and biological worlds are merging in a manner which represents both the possibility of reaching our human potential, and yet at the same time the risk of even greater division and inequality. We now need a new worldview where economics and ecology are in harmony and shift to a life-enhancing approach to the way in which we work and live.

IV. Planet

Our current lifestyles and economic systems, which provide little resilience in the face of global pandemics and other systemic shocks, no longer serve humanity nor our planet. The environment and our ecosystems do not behave in a predictable and linear manner. This suggests that, in relation to how we live our lives, we need to tread carefully and cautiously, because we are not able to predict the outcome of our actions. Businesses and investors, however, often rush into new markets and into new countries which have rich natural resources to exploit, with no thought about the wider implications. We therefore need to shift our collective mindsets and corporate cultures to one of 'active stewardship' of our planet's ecosystems.[50]

FIGURE 2.1 The New 4Ps

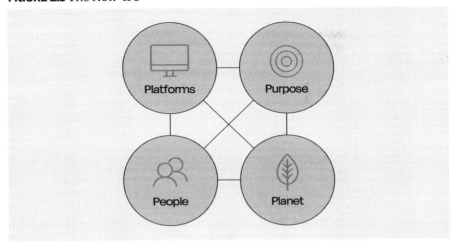

In order to be able to transform visions into reality, deep thinking, one of the four key pillars of Deep Tech, is needed to help organisations understand how to transform our mindsets from thinking about advanced technology towards understanding the impact and power of systemic Deep Tech solutions. People in organisations need to be taught how to implement the New 4Ps by understanding mindset at the deepest level—the ethics, ways of seeing, creativity and systems thinking—while also contributing to the training and development of deeply talented people.

What exactly does this mean in practice? The first thing that visionary leaders can do is to genuinely question the nature of the essential purpose of their organisation, asking if it really is authentic and for the wider good of society and our planet. Andy Last, CEO of Salt Communications, coined one of the most powerful ways to examine our purpose, by asking the question, "Why do we exist and what would people miss if we were no longer to exist?"[51]

The New 4Ps are a synthesis which form the basis of decision-making in an organisation, providing the direction of the development of more prosperous and flourishing business models and value propositions. Once we are clear about our purpose, we are better able to then evaluate our approach to platform design. The reason is that we have reached a stage in the evolution of our technology which has now given us a chance to rectify the shortfalls in our previous economic systems, ones which generated poverty, inequality and the degradation of our natural ecosystems. Locating this vision of platform design inside of the New

4Ps framework provides leaders with an opportunity to consider new forms of organisation, funding, investment and value.

Platforms connect brands and organisations to their audiences by amplifying their purposes. Brands and organisations want people to hear their message and connect with their purpose, but this will only happen if they are genuinely authentic. And to be authentic, organisations need to live their values. When brands and organisations say one thing, but mean another and act in opposition to their stated values and purposes, consumers, employees and activists can and will amplify their voices of opposition through the very same platforms, often being able to create systemic change and improvements to poor business practices.

As we saw in chapter one, the values of Deep Tech as stated in our manifesto are peace, truth, love, righteousness and non-violence. In the following section, we will introduce you to a cutting-edge design studio from São Paulo who are creating value through the New 4Ps by actively integrating these universal human values into their daily practices and organisational culture.

UNIVERSAL HUMAN VALUES

In 2018, 1STi and Holonomics came together to discuss the question of what it means to be human in a technological world; a question which is now more pertinent than ever before. Our idea was to discover new ways to learn how to collaborate and work together to solve our most pressing and complex problems and to find ways to use technology for the greater good of humanity so that we can all flourish and continue to prosper. Our Deep Tech Network therefore began to take shape in the city of São Paulo, launching with our first edition of the Deep Tech Talks, a live event with the theme of *Technology with Soul*. This was followed in 2019 with the second event where we discussed *Augmented Agility* (both concepts of which are explained in detail in chapter six).

The Deep Tech Talks were created to bring together executives, leaders and professionals who were invited to contemplate more deeply on the need to align the human potential of organisations with rapid technological developments. We facilitated these dialogues as an invitation for us to reflect on who we are, our life in society and the future we want to help build. Our aim was to provide meaningful insights into emerging strategies that are inspiring companies to become more adaptive and dynamic in order to continue to evolve in more conscious and sustainable ways.

The universal human values form a fundamental part of our Deep Tech manifesto. The reason is that in order for Deep Tech to become a way of being, we first have to discover that which our essence truly is. It is not sufficient simply to discuss human values and declare them publicly. Transformation happens when they are fully manifested in our lives and therefore fully lived.

The five universal human values of peace, truth, love, righteousness and non-violence can be found in many different cultural traditions and several of the oldest writings in humanity, forming the basis of any healthy and prosperous human social system. We can think of ourselves as the manifestation of these values, and so they define and characterise the highest nature of humanity. When we express each of these five interrelated values, we are being human in the fullest essence. So when we move away from who we are, we end up experiencing that which a lack of human values represents, for example anxiety, fear, insecurity, impatience and intolerance.

Talking about universal values therefore means rescuing all that is most precious in us, especially at a time when we are facing great challenges but also the opportunity to change. When we encounter and interact with the world around us guided by these principles, we value ourselves, become resilient, develop greater creativity, improve our ability to learn and are better able to deal with changes, challenges and adversities in life, while being better able to enjoy our more quiet moments and positive times.

Living the universal values allows us to more fully understand the underlying reasons for someone's behaviour and why that person is acting in a particular way.[52] When you live the values, you can see more about a situation. One way to understand this is through the analogy of the ocean—what happens at the surface and what it is like below. At the depths of the ocean all is tranquil and calm, but as a result of the wind, temperature, pressure and many other factors, the surface can be agitated, choppy, and at times, turbulent. This analogy teaches us that while we are all the same in our essence, on the surface we are different, since we all have different experiences in life and we live in different circumstances, for example.

If we only relate to what we see on the surface, we can potentially end up acting in opposition to the five values, such as judging people superficially and ending up with conflicts, arguments and harmful behaviour. In these instances, the result is instability, confusion, unhappiness, dissatisfaction and inequality. The universal human values lie in the depth of the ocean, enabling us to develop a level of consciousness which allows us to understand that while others are different on the surface, we all share the same essence. When we connect with people, no matter who they may be or how they are acting, we have an ability to connect with their essence.

Universal human values are no less important in virtual or digital interactions as they are in physical interactions. With a move into hybrid working models, where people spend more time at home each week and less time in offices or other places of work, they will need continued support and encouragement to develop healthy organisational cultures. For example, a study led by Zhenyu Yuan, a University of Illinois Chicago researcher, shows that dealing with rude emails at work can create lingering stress and take a toll on people's well-being and family life.[53] The research suggests that impolite emails can have a negative effect on work responsibilities, productivity, and can even be linked to insomnia at night, which can further engender negative emotions the next morning.

Recognising universal human values as the highest expression of humanity changes our approach to the way in which we think about, design and implement technology. These values are present in our manifesto as a way of recognising that technology alone cannot solve our global issues no matter how advanced it may be. Technology is not deep if universal human values are not present. For this reason it is interesting to examine the path that a Brazilian design company has taken in their journey into Deep Tech, as their founders recognised very early on that their first step would need to be the inclusion of universal human values in their strategy.

Pravy is a design house focused on digital innovation, helping organisations to become future-fit through creating, evolving and amplifying digital products through authentic value propositions (a future-fit business is one that in no way undermines the possibility that humans and other life will flourish on earth forever,[54] a concept we explain further in chapter four). The company was founded in 2013 by Rodrigo Linck and Roberto Del Grande as the result of a fusion of Think Tanks Brasil, a marketing agency, and Oxy Mind, a digital production studio.

As Rodrigo explains: "We focus on developing long-term and meaningful relationships with our clients, accompanying them every step of the way to help them grow and achieve new levels of impact. We deliver this transformation by combining our creative digital production experience with advanced design structures and methodologies such as The New 4Ps, the Holonomics Approach with universal human values and the *Customer Experiences with Soul* framework—all of which contribute to achieving authentic and purposeful solutions".

Right from the very start, Rodrigo and Roberto had "dreamed of creating an authentic company, with a genuine purpose and values—a place that brought together people who do what they love while being who they truly are". They sought a name that could expresses this authenticity, arriving at the word 'pravy' which means 'genuine' in Czech.

To accompany this primary value of being genuine, Pravy began a collaborative project with all team members to expand this single value into the expression of a set of values that they were living in their daily lives. They identified the following additional four values:

• We are empathic
• We are creative
• We are innovators
• We are collaborative

In 2020, Rodrigo began to look at the way in which Pravy could evolve to become truly future-fit. Having started to work with Holonomics to implement the *Customer Experiences with Soul* and New 4Ps frameworks, Rodrigo started to explore the way in which they could take inspiration from the universal human values in order to update their values and develop their approach to Deep Tech design initiatives.

As Rodrigo continues: "We design platforms and content every day and feel responsible for the impact they have on people's lives. When Pravy was introduced to the Holonomics Approach, we realised that in expressing the essential nature of the human condition, universal human values are the fundamental requirements for the development of healthy human systems. Experiencing and practicing these values in our work has enabled us to develop both Deep Tech solutions and digital content based on genuine human systems".

The universal human values represent the fundamental values which are expressed through 'situational values' (Figure 2.2). In order to arrive at Pravy's core values, Rodrigo spent time contemplating both the universal and situational human values together.

The situational values help to explain what each universal human value means in practice. The values should not be approached in a fragmented manner. When thinking about one particular universal value or situational value, it is possible to see that all of the others are also present. Pravy developed their own unique set of values by first thinking about which of the universal and situational values best expressed the differing dimensions of Pravy's essence and being (Table 2.1).

FIGURE 2.2 The Universal Human Values

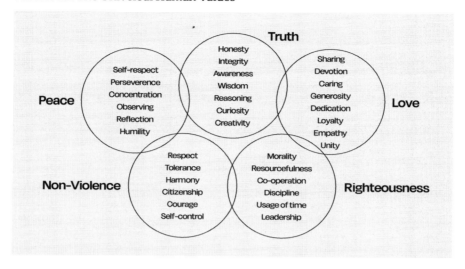

With the universal human values inspiring their new organisational values, we were interested to hear from Rodrigo what the impact had been:

"The deepest impact that we noticed at the start was seeing how we became more aware of our words and people's reactions to them. We have often had to strive to act on values, truly live them, but it has been rewarding to see the positive impact it has had on our relationships with our clients and our partners. In our projects, we observe ourselves reflecting more profoundly on the effect that our creations can have on people's lives and we are now much more conscious by always trying to make decisions oriented by these values and not just personal opinions or preferences. The Deep Tech approach and the New 4Ps were the missing pieces to bring cohesion to our value propositions, demonstrating to our clients in a clear manner the authenticity and meaning that we always look for to help them amplify their own missions, visions and values."

When we shift our thinking from the organisational level to that of the economy, the question is more profound than simply attempting to find the best economic model. Historically, the implementation of economic models has not solved our global problems and has resulted in injustices such as human poverty. The most important element of an economic model is that which is behind it, and we believe that the fundamental basis for any economy is the New 4Ps. An authentic

TABLE 2.1 Pravy's Values

	Love	Love / Non-violence	Truth	Love	Righteousness	Righteousness	Peace
Universal Human Values	Love	Love Non-violence	Truth	Love	Righteousness	Righteousness	Peace
Situational Values	Honesty Integrity	Co-operation Dedication Empathy Devotion Sharing Unity Generosity Loyalty Care	Creativity Commonsense Curiosity Lucidity	Loyalty Co-operation Dedication Empathy Unity Generosity Care Devotion Sharing	Ingenuity Discipline Morality Leadership Use of time Generosity Co-operation	Ingenuity Discipline Morality Leadership Use of time Generosity Co-operation	Reflection Observation Self-respect Perseverance Humility Concentration
Pravy's Values	We are genuine	The strength of empathy	We are free to create	We do together	We lead for the success of everyone	Flexible discipline	We are optimistic in uncertainties
In practice	We believe that genuine people are true, honest with themselves and honest with others. They are reliable, loyal and know how to express their ideas and opinions frankly, being sensitive to the context with authenticity. We don't cling to or remain attached to opinions, as that would be giving up the truth itself.	People are at the heart of everything we do, and understanding people is the key to creating effective solutions. To be empathic is to project yourself into the personality of the other with the genuine intention of helping. This intention at the service of others allows us to identify the pains that generate disharmony and imbalance in people's lives.	Inventing, innovating and producing is part of our nature. To create it is necessary to be lucid, define a purpose and be clear when channelling ideas, like a mirror that reflects the inspirations of the abstract into the concrete world. And for this it is necessary to have courage, to allow yourself to make mistakes without fear of judgment.	Collaborating we build a unified collective understanding, which feeds on our individual repertoire and allows us to create even more powerful ideas. For this we need to express ourselves clearly, showing attention while listening, with the intention of using what has been said as the foundation that will serve to form the solution we are building together.	We believe that collective benevolence in being concerned with the growth and happiness of all is related to the spirit of leadership and sense of ownership that we have. Taking the initiative and taking responsibility for our part, without leaving anyone behind, maintains a bond of trust between us and strengthens us to work collaboratively.	We see discipline as a virtue that makes it possible to materialise our ideas, understanding it as a central axis that animates us towards our goals. In a practical way, discipline gives us more freedom, because it helps to structure our time through the conscious organisation of our actions, establishing the rhythm and frequency that will help us to bring our ideas to fruition.	We step into unfamiliar territories all the time, facing adversities with optimism and perseverance. Understanding this dynamic sharpens our reflection and leads us to a deeper analysis of the causes and effects of adversity. This awareness elevates us to a state of peace and balance, allowing us to be humble and patient in finding the way to solve problems.

purpose which genuinely seeks to do good for people and our planet can provide a path for taking society and human systems to a higher level of dignity and quality of life. When there is a preoccupation with the planet, people will be able to thrive inside of the natural ecosystems in which our economies are embedded. This can be achieved through platforms as a key enabling factor.

When the New 4Ps are present in reflections about the long term of both economics and organisational strategy, they are able to provide a meaningful direction for politicians and business leaders of countries, resulting in new forms of thinking about the nature of wealth, the design of value propositions and the evolution of enterprises. When informed by universal human values, the New 4Ps act as a decision-making framework for the development of prosperous and flourishing economic systems, driven by the logic and architectures of Deep Tech platforms.

DEEP IMPACT THROUGH COLLABORATION IN EDUCATION

Collaboration is a fundamental aspect of both the natural world and the world of technology. It can be both naturally spontaneous as well as being highly organised. However, this does not mean that merely by combining these two attributes of spontaneity and organisation we can reach our goals and achieve our higher aims. Throughout history we have seen many times the dangers of collaboration where human values were not present.

Any form of collaboration therefore must be intentional, so that we can best understand how to connect, co-operate and work together for the collective good and achieve the impact that so many of us are seeking to realise. As Fabro Steibel, executive director of the Rio de Janeiro Institute of Technology and Society observes: "At times it can seem that collaboration is a concept for the future, but the major problems that we have today are a result of questions of collaboration. The architecture of the internet is based on open participation and the world wide web has allowed people to form startups, generate knowledge through Wikipedia—the possibilities are endless. But in many ways the internet can also be thought of as a microcosmos of society. If certain segments of society are excluded, such as low income families, then the internet simply becomes a substrate of society. We need to think of what a fully humanised internet could be like, being genuinely open and equal for all".[55]

Leaders who seek to foster a truly open, democratic and authentic spirit of collaboration in their organisations must first understand their own leadership styles and their underlying quality of consciousness that determines the quality of their relationships with all of those with whom they have contact and with whom their decisions impact upon. The New 4Ps are of direct relevance to this context, in that for collaboration to be successful, the purpose has to be extremely clear. This is the case for Wikipedia, in that each person participating has a clear and coherent role in that which the collaboration is aiming to achieve.

While confronting the great humanitarian crisis of the Covid-19 pandemic, we also saw a natural awakening of the desire to help and to collaborate. This is a manifestation of an expansion of consciousness and of humanity's true essence, with human values being fully present, enabling people to make advances in the way in which they are able to collaborate through platforms and networks in the virtual world. So when the purpose of an initiative is genuine and people value openness, many great problems and difficulties can be overcome.

An example can be seen in União Rio, a voluntary civil society movement which brings together people and non-governmental organisations that are committed to their community and state.[56] Vai na Web, a not-for-profit movement founded by 1STi, participated in this initiative to provide humanitarian support during the Covid-19 pandemic in Rio de Janeiro, by building a platform which could provide transparency for donors, thereby enabling them to monitor their donations and ensure that their humanitarian aid was reaching families in vulnerable situations in the most intelligent and agile manner possible.

The distribution of food aid to the favelas in Rio de Janeiro presents many logistical challenges, especially due to the presence of armed conflict in many of these territories. Young talented programmers and digital designers from the very communities being impacted and who were educated through Vai na Web's technology programme built the advanced União Rio platform and distribution algorithms in collaboration with a number of government organisations and other initiatives which provided real-time streams of data. Together this networked supply chain was able to create a tracking system in just a matter of weeks which could deliver emergency food baskets across the metropolitan region during a state of emergency.

The impact of deep technologies comes from deep thinking and an ability to understand the power of systemic solutions. So for example the União Rio platform has the potential to be amplified further into an architectural backbone (a technology concept which we explain in chapter four) which can form the basis of launching further humanitarian services such as improving water sanitation, another major challenge for many of the world's largest metropolitan regions.

In order to achieve the greatest systemic impact possible, the ventures which we are developing inside of our Deep Tech ecosystem have a focus on health, education, collaboration platforms and computational sensemaking (a concept we explain in chapter six). For example, Vai na Web is helping to overcome inequality in education through developing deeply talented individuals from disadvantaged social backgrounds through its innovative Social Impact as a Service Model (a business model we explain in chapter seven). One of the projects which designers and coders from Vai na Web are working on, along with Holonomics and 1STi, is Almanaque Digital, which is transforming the way we think about education and how high-quality education can be offered in a digital context.

Almanaque Brasil is a project which was originally conceived in 1999 by Elifas Andreato, one of Brazil's most important and prolific graphical designers. He was born in Paraná in 1946 and started his career at Editora Abril, where he helped to set up numerous magazines and journals such as *Placar*, *Veja* and *História da Música Popular Brasileira*. It is as an artist that Elifas is most widely known, having designed around four hundred album covers for virtually all of the greatest artists in Brazilian music such as Chico Buarque, Elis Regina, Maria Bethânia, Toquinho, Vinícius de Moraes, Paulinho da Viola, Tom Zé, Rolando Boldrin and Renato Teixeira.

From the very start of his career in publishing, Elifas realised the power that paper had, through the platform of publishing, to amplify his audience as an artist:

"While I was learning at the editorial rooms, I would watch newsmen multiply their opinions and articles, from the printing, to the rotary press and then on to the news-stands. This was one of the most important lessons of the many provided by these co-creators: paper was the support of original work, also uniquely serving to render the work available to thousands of people. It was at that time that I realised I would never create paintings, that my art would have to be perceived by all eyes, by all sensitivities, and never confine itself to being hung on single walls. In this way, paper would provide me with the unlimited reproduction of any drawing. Whatever I created would be seen by all."[57]

Elifas has always been conscious of the purpose that he sought his art to play:

"My art is linked to the story of my life as well as those lives that are like mine; it also serves to relate what I, and people similar to me, believe the world to be; a world of justice and freedom. This is how this journey must be called to mind: the total sum of impressions engraved on a paper trail that started in Paraná to end I know not where. What I learned, as a self-taught artist, I placed at the service of what my beliefs were, never exchanging them for a better offer."[58]

With these values and his artistic consciousness guiding his life decisions, the idea of Almanaque Brasil came to Elifas as a way to preserve the history, culture and traditions of Brazil. Brazil is a soulful country whose people have historically been resilient, caring, creative, dynamic and deeply talented. It is this incredibly rich history of his country's culture, science, sport, music, biographies and literature that Elifas began to capture, write about and illustrate in the Almanaque magazine which was published between 1999 and 2015. In this period eighteen million copies were published, reaching 72 million people through distribution on TAM aircraft, a Brazilian national airline (now LATAM). The Almanaque initiative would reach an even wider audience in 2007 with the launch of their television programme which aired on TV Cultura and TV Brasil channels, resulting in fifty-two episodes and five books being published between 2005 and 2017.

The publishing of Almanaque Brasil in physical print came to an end in 2015. This prompted Elifas and his son Bento Andreato to start exploring ways of taking the project into the digital world, creating a blog and a Facebook page where they would continue to curate texts, games, quizzes and other content. By chance, Maria and Simon met Elifas in São Paulo at an exhibition in 2019, starting a conversation which would lead to the ideation and evolution of Almanaque Brasil, which resulted in the development of Almanaque Digital, a Deep Tech educational platform to help solve the myriad educational challenges of improving the level of engagement and the quality of education in Brazil.

The aim of Almanaque Digital is simple—to ensure that each child and teenager in Brazil has access to its encyclopaedic library of content through its Deep Tech educational platform and applications in order for them to be able to learn new knowledge and skills effectively. It aims to do so by supporting teachers in the development of more effective learning methods, increasing parental involvement and improving the way in which student learning is assessed.

There are a number of interrelated areas in which Almanaque Digital is aiming to achieve results from the perspective of students based on the Brazilian National Curricula guidelines:

- Knowledge
- Scientific, critical and creative thinking
- Cultural repertoire
- Communication
- Digital Culture
- Reasoning skills
- Self-knowledge and self-care
- Empathy and co-operation
- Responsibility and citizenship[59]

And in relation to teachers, the initiative is being developed to help with providing:

- A more creative curriculum
- Interdisciplinary skills
- Access to technology
- Parents involved
- Increased student performance

Elifas has noted that some of his friends have questioned him about the relevance of his project which seeks to protect the national memory of Brazil, saying that the format of the Almanaque was simply not compatible with the modernity of new platforms and the velocity of information. His reply is simple: "The past which is unknown when revealed is new!"[60]

By producing a rich repository of short-form stories, anecdotes, games, quizzes, articles and animations, the result is content perfectly suited to mobile devices and rendering for applications for young people. Almanaque Digital is being supported by sponsoring organisations who are aiming to create bespoke editions for specific communities and audiences, thereby helping disadvantaged children and young adults to fully engage in their education and be inspired by many of the most illustrious Brazilians.

The platform applications are being produced by young developers from Vai na Web, thereby creating a virtuous circle of support in which organisations help communities which in turn results in Vai na Web being able to support the technical education of even more young Brazilians. In this manner, the Almanaque Digital project is able to create a systemic form of social impact which can be scaled and amplified across the entire country.

Bento Andreato is a cultural entrepreneur and managing director of the Elifas Andreato Institute. For Bento, Almanaque Digital is an opportunity to help Brazilians recover their sense of place, both in relation to their social and ecological connections not only with Brazil, but also with their neighbourhoods, towns and local regions:

"Almanaque Brasil was created with the objective of bringing Brazil to Brazilians, through examples of both well-known personalities and unheard of but fascinating people, creating the possibility of learning from the greatest examples of our people and rich culture. Almanaque Digital has created the opportunity to reach people living in rural communities, many of which are often impacted by industrial activities, creating the opportunity to raise the self-esteem of those people who need it most. By helping people across the entire country to get in touch with the great riches that Almanaque Digital can bring to them, we can help them to feel that they belong to the larger group of people who have made and are making a difference in the lives of us all."

The evolution of Almanaque into a Deep Tech project has enabled Elifas and Bento to realise their vision of transforming education in Brazil. It is far more than simply a channel to deliver content digitally. It is a way of designing curated and illustrated content in a manner that can be personalised to individual communities and designated groups, thereby helping them to develop a deeper sense of place and of their identities as their education progresses. It is clear to see the emotional as well as professional impact this project has had on Elifas:

"Almanaque Brasil has been my life mission. For fifteen years we were able to impact millions of people who traveled aboard TAM with our in-flight magazines which brought together rich and varied content about our Brazilian culture. That we are now able to make Almanaque available through applications and a digital platform is a source of great joy for me, as the digital environment is now so critical for our educational and entertaining content to be able to reach young people.

"Even I, a 75 year old person, am able to inhabit this universe. What this means is that the Almanaque can be both traditional in its purpose without losing its relevance, and now as a platform available in many different modes—magazines, television, books and applications. Being able to evolve Almanaque through Deep Tech while maintaining our DNA has allowed us to ensure that it can be continually updated, personalised and remain as relevant as it always was, now reaching people from every region across the whole of Brazil. Long live Almanaque Brasil!"

Almanaque Digital embodies the complete essence of the New 4Ps, evolving from print media and television into a platform with purpose, designed to help people develop self-esteem, a sense of place and a positive impact on the planet through education and helping communities learn how to flourish and thrive locally, through the support of sponsoring organisations. And additionally, the project is an example of Social Impact as a Service, an integral dimension of the platform's value proposition which we explain in detail in chapter seven.

Executive Summary

→ Deep Tech is a new economic model based on the New 4Ps of platforms, purpose, people and planet. The New 4Ps are the fundamental requirements for the development of healthy organisational systems. The universal human values are the foundation of what being human truly means.

→ The New 4Ps is a practical and inclusive framework to help people understand the major trends shaping business ecosystems and the importance of a holistic approach to creating a high impact strategy. They provide a new set of economic principles for organisations wishing to transform themselves digitally and culturally, and can be utilised prior to any design, strategy and marketing initiatives.

→ Pravy is a cutting-edge design studio from São Paulo which is creating value through the New 4Ps by actively integrating universal human values into their daily practices and organisational culture. When the universal human values are present in an organisation, people flourish and contribute to the development of our capacity for reinvention and adaptation, enhancing our creativity, critical thinking, collaboration and communication.

→ Almanaque Digital, an example of the New 4Ps in practice, is a unique platform which brings together the best of Brazilian culture and history in a beautiful way, with a strong focus on the stories of the country's most important artists, writers and musicians. It is a Deep Tech project that is helping to transform education in Brazil by helping teachers to create more effective learning methods and increasing parental involvement. It aims to help children, young adults and communities learn how to thrive, prosper and develop a sense of place and higher purpose.

3

The Living Dimension
of Technology

LIVING SYSTEMS

In every aspect of our lives we encounter systems and yet our educational institutions in general do not teach transdisciplinary systems thinking as a fundamental skill and ability. There are many approaches to understanding systems, including the notion that many systems are in fact mental constructs whose boundaries are delimited by our mental models, paradigms, metaphors and cognitive biases.

Michael C. Jackson has developed Critical Systems Thinking as an evaluative framework to help leaders be in the best position to deal with the level of complexity in their decision making. It explores the strengths and weaknesses of the various approaches found in both systems thinking and complexity theory, and how to employ them in combination.[61] Jackson provides an example of Critical Systems Thinking in practice in relation to the Covid-19 pandemic in the UK, explaining that: "the way we understand complexity makes a huge difference to how we respond to crises of this type. Inadequate conceptualisations of complexity lead to poor responses that can make matters worse".[62] For this reason, it is important for leaders to take into account the many different approaches to understanding complex systems and the resulting strategies that can be deployed.

Gareth Morgan described eight different metaphors for the way in which we can think about organisations: machines, organisms, brains, cultural systems, political systems, psychic prisons, instruments of domination, and flux and transformation.[63] Each one of these metaphors has specific contexts in which they work and contexts in which they do not apply. When these metaphors are made explicit, leaders can better make sense of their organisations through developing new ways of seeing and exploring the impact of people's different perspectives.

The Western educational paradigm teaches us how to break systems down into their conceptual parts, but it does not teach us how to encounter the wholeness of the phenomenon we wish to understand. Our educational institutions are still highly compartmentalised, existing as separate academic departments which rarely converse. The issue is that we need neither a new theory of systems or nor a necessity to develop even more advanced technology to help us solve our current systemic issues. Science and technology have made great leaps of progress through the development of innovations of immense complexity. Our collective knowledge and understandings of ecological, mechanical, technological and human systems is immense. Our problems come about when we apply a limited approach or no systemic approach at all to understanding these interwoven and hyperconnected systems.

Recognising these challenges of introducing systems thinking into organisations at the most senior level, the Holonomics Approach was created in 2011, in order to develop a singular approach to organisational change—one which would not separate digital transformation from cultural transformation.[64] The challenge for leaders is that in order to instigate this transformation, they too need to change the paradigms informing their mental models. Only then can an organisation achieve concrete changes to their predominant organisational paradigm.

The focus of the Holonomics Approach is to help business leaders and managers learn how to respond, adapt and communicate in new and innovative ways through developing new ways of seeing, expanding their form of consciousness and helping to nurture the living of universal human values in their organisations. Digital transformation initiatives are not separated from cultural transformation initiatives due to the fact that organisations are living systems, where structured business processes and work flows are interwoven with human flows of meaning, feelings, sensing, conversation, interpretation, power, politics, friendship, visions, values and purposes.

Business choices are made from a vastly complex web of competing systems, for example human emotion, social pressures, market research, multiple data sources and business models. The ethos of the Holonomics Approach, amidst such complexity, is therefore to help businesses to see the whole system.

We can summarise the evolution of thinking that Holonomics fosters in people in the table below:

TABLE 3.1 Holonomic Thinking

Ego-nomic	Holonomic
Generation why?	Generation why
Internet of things	Technology with soul
Selfie	Hologram
Fraction	Fractal
Piece	Whole

Mechanical metaphors, while still relevant to their specific context, continue to predominate in management thinking and in the implementation of business practices such as process reengineering and business redesign. While science still does not have a singular and definitive way to characterise life, we can of course appreciate living systems as having the following qualities:

TABLE 3.2 Living Systems

dynamic	cognitive
creative	self-organising
ordered, complex *and* chaotic	dissipative
co-operative and competitive	evolving
unpredictable yet understandable	diverse
emergent	replicating and reproducing

There are many different barriers to business and political leaders being able to develop systems thinking skills, and for this reason one of the fundamental elements of the Holonomics Approach is to first help leaders develop new ways of seeing before they attempt to implement systemic change in their organisations. There are many different ways of thinking about the parts and wholes in systems, and if these differences are not fully understood, any change methodology or framework being applied will not function as expected, even if it was designed using systemic principles.

We can think about the parts of a system and their relationship to the system as a whole in the following ways:

- As the parts being mechanically interconnected;
- As the parts representing the whole in some manner;
- As the relationships between the parts;
- As the processes which emerge due to the relationships between the parts;
- As the synergies which arise from processes;
- As parts which are rule-obeying members of higher-level systems;
- As systems which are embedded within greater systems;
- As cognitive flows of information between the parts;
- As flows of meaning between the parts;
- As entities which have their identity due to being part of a greater whole.

From this list it is possible to see that while we need analytical and intellectual abilities to understand and build certain forms of system, we also need to access other ways of knowing the world in order to encounter living systems and develop an embodied way of experiencing wholeness and the interconnectedness of life. We have to be mindful about which form of systems thinking we are working with and we also need to be mindful about when we are using analytical frameworks to artificially delineate systems which in reality are more complex, open and unbounded than the models which describe them.

Our modern business world is currently dominated by technology and a logical, rational and symbolic way of thinking which gives us a sensation of being separate from the world; both from other people and the natural ecosystems of which we are a part. It is this sense of separation that allows people to inflict harm and damage on other people and on our ecosystems without sensing, feeling and intuiting the highly-coupled and interwoven connectedness to them. In order to solve our complex problems we require a higher level of consciousness that encompasses the four ways of knowing.[65]

In Figure 3.1 *feeling* is located opposite to *thinking*. Feeling is not emotion. It is through feeling that we achieve a sense of connection to other people and to nature. *Sensing* is the way of knowing of artists, photographers, painters and chefs. Whereas sensory knowing is very concrete, *intuition* provides us with a much deeper sense of the meaning of the phenomena we encounter in our lived experiences as human beings. It is responsible for insights, scientific discoveries and new ways of seeing.

FIGURE 3.1 The Four Ways of Knowing

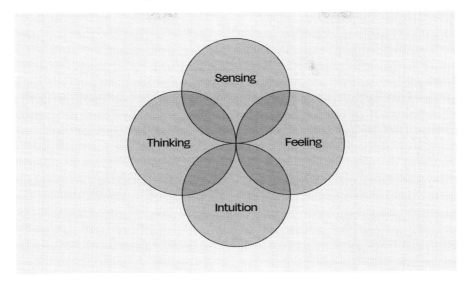

From the era of industrialisation to our modern age of advanced technology, our ways of knowing the world have become out of balance. Research from psychiatrist Iain McGilchrist suggests that the two hemispheres of our divided brain operate in profoundly different ways, but not as we realise.[66] The left hemisphere provides instrumental attention. This allows us to manipulate objects and use things for our benefit. But this type of attention is narrowly focussed and it means that we experience reality as fragmented, static and ultimately lifeless. It is the right hemisphere that provides relational attention, enabling us to see the whole picture, to form social bonds, to inhabit and belong to the world we see, rather than simply being detached from it and using it.[67]

An important insight from McGilchrist is that while our brains are divided, we have the potential ability to explore and experience these differences, and ultimately master them. We do not have to be a prisoner of our left hemispheres. As he explained in a dialogue with Simon:

"The brain is not only deeply divided down the middle (an odd fact, given that both its purpose and its power lies precisely in making connections), but also clearly asymmetrical: the hemispheres reliably differ in size, weight, shape, surface structure, cell architecture in some areas, grey to white matter ratio, response to endocrine hormones and in neurotransmitter profile. Not only that, but much of the neural traffic between hemispheres has an inhibitory function.

"The crude, old ideas that logic and language are in the left, and images and emotions in the right, were exploded long ago. Each hemisphere is involved in absolutely everything we do. As soon as one stops asking the question appropriate to a machine—'what does it do?'—and asks the question appropriate to a person—'in what manner does it do what it does?'—the answer starts to become clearer. Differences between the hemispheres in birds, animals and humans ultimately relate to differences in attention, which have evolved for clear reasons of survival. But since the nature of the attention we bring to bear on the world changes what it is we find there, and since what we find there influences the kind of attention we pay in the future, differences of attention are not just technical, mechanical issues, but have significant human experiential and philosophical consequences. They change the world we inhabit.

"The problem of hemisphere conflict is not primarily about the individual's day to day experience, but about the way individuals conceive—and in the end a culture comes to conceive—the nature of the world in which we live. It is about two 'takes' on the world, one of which, to put it simply and briefly, is concerned with closing down to a certainty and the other concerned with opening up to a possibility. One, therefore (the left), aims to reach one correct answer ('either/or'): the other (the right) is more able to live with ambivalence and the possibility of two apparently incompatible possibilities being true ('both/and'). In an era which prizes consistency within a system of thinking above fidelity to the sometimes irresolvable complexities of the real world, one of these 'takes' can become comparatively neglected."[68]

There is growing evidence to show that perceptual processes are influenced by culture, and these perceptual processes in turn impact on how we understand and think about systems. People in western cultures have been found to organise objects by emphasising rules and categories and focusing on salient objects regardless of context, while people in East Asian cultures are more inclined to rely less on formal logic and use more intuitive modes of thinking, responding to context and the relationships between objects and their contexts. In one study, American and Japanese students were asked to describe what they saw in a number of images, such as a fish tank. They found that while the two groups talked about the most prominent objects in the foreground (the fish, which were colourful and swam around), Japanese students also tended to talk and recall more information about the images in the background.[69]

Reductionist thinking is not the problem. The use of frameworks is not the problem. The problem is not being aware of the different ways of knowing the world and of being mindful when we are implementing a framework from one particular perspective and level of consciousness. When we are both mindful of the manner in which we are deploying and using systemic frameworks and have mastery over all four ways of knowing, then we have more degrees of freedom in relation to how we act in the world and how we make sense and respond to our environment.

MAPPING STRATEGY SYSTEMICALLY

When a framework is well-designed, it can facilitate systemic thinking in an organisational context and be implemented in an agile manner across a whole business ecosystem. Our ability to perceive, understand and actively work with a systemic framework depends on developing a dynamic way of seeing, the level of our consciousness and the presence of human values. In implementing digital transformation programmes executives first need to have a clear and systemic understanding of their strategy. One way in which this can be achieved is through the design and execution of the Balanced Scorecard management tool, developed by Robert Kaplan and David Norton.[70]

Maria worked directly with Kaplan and Norton implementing Balanced Scorecard in many of the largest and most important enterprises in Brazil. This direct experience of helping to evolve the methodology with the creators provided her with firsthand knowledge of the way in which the Balanced Scorecard has an educational role, allowing people to see the relationships which exist between the different areas and activities within organisations. It therefore develops a way of seeing in organisations based on systemic vision, as opposed to the siloed and fragmented view which more normally predominates.

Balanced Scorecard is a methodology which enables a company to look at itself in a more balanced and systemic way, including both the long and short term. It is much more than just a tool for organising indicators; it is a way of managing and enabling an organisation to look at itself from a more integrated and multi-dimensional perspective. Balanced Scorecard links financial measures to operational measures, and translates organisational strategy into four classical perspectives: the financial perspective, the customer perspective, the internal perspective and the learning and growth perspective. Its impact has been to expand the focus of businesses from concentrating purely on shareholder value to include customer, people, process, community and ecological dimensions as well.[71]

The methodology is relevant not only to the design of single enterprises, but also to educational, governmental, sustainability and innovation ecosystems. As Kaplan explains:

"In today's networked and global world, collaboration across organisational boundaries has become a critical competency for innovation and success. Solving complex problems for customers or for society can rarely be accomplished using capabilities only within a single enterprise, whether an individual company or a government ministry. Co-creating a strategy map and Balanced Scorecard helps to align multiple entities to a holistic, shared vision for success."[72]

Maria's work in recent years has been to develop the Balanced Scorecard methodology by teaching leaders how to use it to create agile strategies to align and orchestrate their objectives and goals in a systemic manner. This enables executives to learn how to appreciate and understand systems thinking at a much more profound and meaningful level, so that they can then more fully appreciate the shift in paradigm which a successful implementation of Balanced Scorecard entails.

Every methodology has an approach behind it, a way of doing that needs to be respected and taken into account before being implemented. Executives who do not have systemic vision are only able to conceive of Balanced Scorecard as a template-driven methodology. When this happens, goals and indicators are defined by teams and departments in isolation from the organisation as a whole, the idea being that if individual parts are optimised, then the whole organisation will achieve optimal performance as well. The absence of a systemic approach can create many difficulties in practice due to non-aligned goals reducing inter-departmental co-operation and the suboptimal use of resources.

When an organisational culture fosters systemic understanding, the methodology is able to facilitate the development of more agile and creative perspectives, ones which emphasise the active, dynamic and living relationships throughout the organisation. The critical success factor is acceptance of the need for the organisation to change its mindset and expand awareness of itself. In order to build a Balanced Scorecard it is not simply enough to 'implement' a tool or methodology considering only its technical side, methodically constructing it step-by-step. Following stages is only one small part of the equation. The much larger and more significant part of the equation in the implementation of Balanced Scorecard is a movement of change of perception. And to be effective, this must occur at all levels. For this reason, the Holonomics Approach, when applied to agile strategy, develops authenticity, empathy, creativity and the understanding of the lived experience of those working and forming part of the organisation's ecosystem.

Methodologies and advanced technological platforms, systems and applications are not magic wands that will do all the work alone simply by being acquired. The strength of Balanced Scorecard is that it facilitates significant transformation in managers' ability to lead. There is no effective change when we expect others to change but do not change ourselves. So before implementing a Balanced Scorecard it is therefore imperative that a leader truly understands that they will foster a change in the way their organisation perceives itself and the quality of relationships. In the process of the construction of a Balanced Scorecard people learn to see themselves as co-dependents and to see the processes of which they are a part. The process is as important as the result.

The description of an organisation's strategy is contained within a visual model termed the 'strategy map' and as such it represents one of the most important ways in which an organisation becomes more agile and aligned through developing shared vision and understanding across its divisions and departments (Figure 3.2). The strategy map, via different perspectives, makes explicit both the objectives that the organisation wishes to achieve in order to realise its vision of the future, and the internal objectives of the organisation that will enable the desired results to be achieved. Agile-oriented goal systems such as OKRs (objectives and key results, which describe both what an initiative will achieve and how it will be measured) can be aligned with the strategy map which are then tracked and reviewed frequently.

Cause and effect relationships are included in the map in order to demonstrate the interrelations between objectives. Causal relationships are always represented

FIGURE 3.2 Example Strategy map

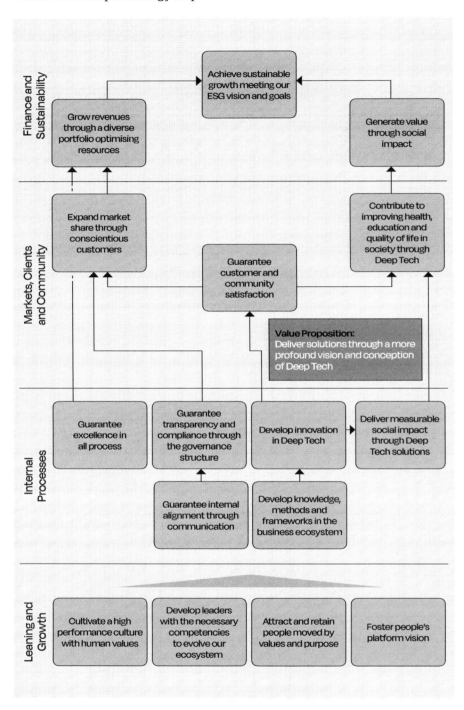

by starting at the bottom and moving upwards, showing that if the internal objectives are achieved, the outcomes will lead to the achievement of the key objectives. This ensures that there is coherence between the objectives which must be understood in an integrated manner and from a systemic point of view.

The aim of a Deep Tech strategy is to elevate organisations to a higher level of actuation. This can be achieved through the development of a platform vision which always starts with an elevated value proposition. A value proposition is a statement of how your product or service will benefit your customer. It clearly defines what you will do for your ideal customer and why you're better than your competitors.

Because the value proposition is the heart of the strategy it is located in the Markets, Clients and Community perspective of the map, emphasising that if the organisation is fully able to achieve its strategy, it will fully deliver on its promise to customers and wider stakeholders. It is this value proposition which embodies the purpose of the organisation and which drives and directs people and internal processes towards delivering this promise of value.

The power of mapping strategy systemically comes from enabling people to understand the why, how and where behind who and what impacts on them, and subsequently how their behaviours and actions impact on others. People become more committed to the strategy and are better able to develop consensus, two key pillars of Balanced Scorecard. This is because the strategy map provides a coherent narrative for leaders to communicate. As Kaplan puts it, "The very act of translating the strategy into a strategy map transforms people".[73]

Balanced Scorecard can be seen as an entire management system, but many systemic aspects can be easily missed when implementing it. While many businesses and organisations still aim to just maximise the performance of separate parts such as teams, divisions and profit centres through OKRs, Balanced Scorecard allows leaders to orchestrate the parts by using the map to help encourage people not just to maximise their best locally, but to do what is best for the overall strategy, which represents the vision and purpose of the organisation. The result is a leadership culture which is based on facilitating a relational and interconnected form of management which enables agility to emerge naturally and in a way that involves everyone.

With this more systemic vision of the entire organisation, resources can be reallocated to any problematic aspect of the organisation which requires the most effort and attention. One of the key activities is the communication of the strategy to all members of the organisation, which can also include wider stakeholders and representatives from the communities with which an organisation impacts. Bringing people into the process creates meaning for them, allowing them to understand the relationship between the individual elements and the whole strategy. There are many organisations where leaders do not include design and development teams in the strategic process, thereby preventing them from developing strategic awareness. For this reason, we have developed a Deep Tech Discovery process (explained in the following chapter) that enhances agile design through the inclusion of visual and communication-driven agile strategy practices.

Authentic engagement with people is not just through rational thinking, but through feeling, linking them emotionally with the strategy, thereby motivating them and helping them to develop their own performance. Balanced Scorecard is, in essence, a tool that organises conversations, and because of this, the organisation needs to develop competency in promoting and facilitating dialogue. This means that people in companies need to learn how to conduct dialogues and, especially, how to listen. The magic happens in the interactions, not in the business intelligence software that calculates and reports the indicators. A conversation, when done well and which contemplates the rich diversity that exists in the organisation, is what will really make the strategy come alive and ready to be executed and well-managed.

Balanced Scorecard is an open system, in that it encompasses all the issues facing an organisation, such as sustainability and community relationships. The values of the organisation become aligned with the way of doing things—its culture—such as the way of treating customers and suppliers. Every major issue which has an impact on the overall performance can be given the same level of importance as financial matters. For all of these reasons, Balanced Scorecard can contribute to fostering a collective sense of purpose and values in an organisation, when implemented by a conscious leadership and from a wider systemic perspective.

While not every organisation may utilise Balanced Scorecard as a methodology, it is still important, nonetheless, for leaders to understand the systemic principles described in this section behind its design and operation. The reason is that before any organisation starts to design and implement a platform-based business model, it must first start by identifying its core value proposition which it intends to elevate (a process we describe and explain in chapter four). Balanced Scorecard is therefore a way of helping an organisation to develop an agile and living systems approach to strategy by linking and integrating the core value proposition into strategy via the strategy map, thereby ensuring that the strategic drivers for change, value proposition, goals, OKRs, indicators and projects are all aligned. This creates clarity for teams as to which programs should be prioritised and implemented, thereby maximising the performance of the organisation as a whole.

LIVED EXPERIENCE

Businesses normally spend all of their efforts measuring experience through the prism of quantitative and qualitative frameworks, rarely taking the time to contemplate the nature of experience itself. The philosophical practice of exploring 'lived experience' is a powerful way in which this can be achieved. Before we can explore lived experience we have to consider how we normally think about and describe experience from design, business research and lay perspectives. To help us we can look at the way in which artists experience the world and are able to capture the essence of our experiences in such poetically powerful ways.

The song *Mad World* was released in 1982 by Tears for Fears, a two-piece band consisting of Roland Orzabal and Curt Smith. The song was written by Orzabal while he was unemployed and living in an apartment in central Bath, a historical and architecturally beautiful city in the south west of England. The lyrics were inspired both by watching people working 9-to-5 jobs go about their business and also the works of American psychotherapist, Dr. Arthur Janov, the most famous of which was the controversial but best-selling *Primal Scream*.[74] While many fans had interpreted the melancholic lyrics of the song as a reference to suicide, Orzabal recounted how the duo had read Janov's postulation about the way in which our most dramatic dreams release the most tension. Hence the line, "The dreams in which I'm dying are the best I've ever had".

The song has been covered many times, both by professional singers and bands as well as pop-hopefuls on talent shows such as The X Factor and The Voice. One of the most striking interpretations was written and performed by Gary Jules in 2001 when the song formed part of the climatic ending of the film *Donnie Darko*. Twenty years after its release Smith explained how the Jules' version was "amazing to hear when it first came on" feeling that it was truer to the essence of the song than their own version. Jules' musical interpretation was as dark as the lyrics, in comparison with their own electronic style of music, which had made them popular due to "the juxtaposition of quite serious and intense lyrics with a pop sound",[75] a style which had been influenced by artists such as Gary Newman, Depeche Mode and Duran Duran.

Perhaps some of the song's popularity comes from the way in which it talks to our sometimes uncomfortable experiences at school, especially for those having to start a new school mid-term, being the odd one out with no friends. When we think about our memories of youth, how easy is it really to return to exactly the same state of mind we had, many years back when we were someone completely different and still with so much to learn and experience? As Orzabal recalled when hearing Jules' rendition of his song: "That was probably the proudest moment of my career. I was in my 40s and had forgotten how I felt when I wrote all those Tears for Fears songs. I thought thank God for the 19-year-old Roland Orzabal".[76]

New social technologies have rapidly advanced the way in which businesses collect our personal data with a view to understanding our behaviours, attitudes and opinions. And customer experience design practices have advanced through methodologies such as ethnography, empathic research and qualitative analysis. But it is still rare to find an exploration of the nature of experience itself in marketing, innovation and design departments, and almost never at the level of boardrooms. This reflection on the difficulty of recalling our own lived experience from youth shows just how challenging the question is of capturing and understanding the lived experience of others.

For this reason, our Deep Tech approach integrates artistic investigations into our technological, strategic and cultural initiatives in organisations. If we look at psychology as a science, it is in fact a discipline consisting of many and often conflicting and contradictory schools of thought. Consciousness still remains a mystery, and the science of defining and describing experience remains incomplete at best. This is not to criticise psychology, for it has helped us to develop structured approaches to the exploration of human experience. But psychology and cognitive science alone do not have a monopoly on the exploration of our human condition.

An artist such as Gary Jules can immerse himself in the pathos of the lyrics of a song, and with a few notes from a single piano, trigger something deep within us which brings back the experiences we lived so many years ago, lucidly and with all of the emotions and sensations which were embodied and enfolded into them. By comparison, a psychologist aims to remove themselves from the phenomenon being studied in order to avoid extraneous variables impacting on the results obtained. This approach is entirely valid, but it is not the only approach to the understanding of our human condition. Our artistic approach aims to complement formal methods which codify our human experience in written descriptions, for it is impossible to describe the wholeness of our experiences with language, which, while capable of disclosing aspects of reality to us, can also hide reality from us as well.

Working with lived experience in a corporate or organisational context is not necessarily about creating artistic works of art; it is about having the ability to explore experience as it is lived, knowing that our external physical environments as experienced by us in our internal lifeworlds can differ greatly from other people who have had completely different upbringings. Being sensitive to our lived experience means changing how we design digital and cultural transformation initiatives, applying more nuanced, multi-dimensional frameworks and methodologies. This is particularly pertinent in Deep Tech projects during the initial discovery phase, an aspect we explain in more detail in chapter four.

The concept of lived experience comes from phenomenology, a branch of philosophy that explores the way in which the phenomena of our human experience appear as meaningful to us. Philosopher Henri Bortoft explained phenomenology in the following way:

"It's hard to catch hold of because it's like trying to catch something as it's happening and which is over before we can do so. It can perhaps be described most simply as 'stepping back' into where we are already. This means shifting the focus of attention *within experience* away from what is experienced into the experiencing of it. So if we consider seeing, for example, this means that we have to 'step back' from *what* is seen into the *seeing* of what is seen."[77]

While cognitive psychology aims to understand the human mind from the perspective of information processing models, working with lived experience and entering into individual life worlds demonstrates to us the need to always be open to the myriad ways in which the same physical world can be experienced depending on many different individual, collective and social factors. For this reason, the Holonomics Approach has been implemented within customer experience and digital transformation projects to help people explore and enter into the lived experience dimension of organisational life, in order to better understand the human and economic systems in which we are embedded. The *Customer Experiences with Soul* framework was developed to help leaders understand how to integrate lived experience into their design initiatives. The following two case studies illustrate just how powerful this concept can be.

Hospital Sírio-Libanês in São Paulo is one of the most important hospitals in South America. The senior team had spent some years developing their strategy map using Balanced Scorecard as the methodology, with their strategic pillars based around the key drivers of the introduction of advanced technologies, growth through the expansion of new hospital locations, sustainability and medical education supported through a philanthropic business model. With these interconnected dimensions of their strategy complete, the challenge was how to communicate the strategy map to the entire hospital, i.e., every single person at every single level.

Together with the strategy, marketing and HR teams at the hospital, Simon was invited to design a communications event to enable them to better explain their strategy map, with the proposed solution based on gamification and storytelling. The objective was to design an experience that would 'melt the social hierarchy', in other words, break down the social barriers between doctors and senior medical staff and the rest of the organisation in a manner that was not explicitly obvious, in order for each person to be able to develop an empathic understanding of challenges, tasks and lived experiences not normally discussed. One-hour sessions with up to one hundred people sitting at one of ten tables were run, involving 2,500 people in total. Facilitators ensured that each table ended up with a wide mix of collaborators from every area and department in the hospital.[78]

No attempt was made to communicate the strategy map *as* a strategy map; very few people would have understood or related to it in this format. Instead, a sensitivity to the lived experience of the many different backgrounds of collaborators led to the idea of re-designing the strategy map as a story which was printed and laid out across the tables. Normally in this scenario with this composition of people on the tables, the most senior person would naturally take control and read the material to the others present. Because each strategy story filled the length of each table, one person could only read a part. The result was that doctors and surgeons naturally ended up listening to secretaries and nutritionists tell the story of how the hospital aimed to reach their five-year vision, and so the traditional social hierarchies started to melt away into an experience of wholeness.

Those who work in the area of customer experience must always be mindful of the livingness and wholeness within experience, and this applies as much to the employee experience as much as the customer experience. If we only focus on understanding the content of our experience, we miss its more subtle qualitative and dynamic aspects. Designers therefore working with phenomenological methodologies are able to instil in senior managers a more intuitive and felt connection with the customer experience of their products and services, and with the lived experience of their colleagues and stakeholders. And leaders working with lived experience are better equipped to engage people not just through talking about purpose, but by allowing them to gain an embodied experience of the purpose, through active exploration aided by interactions which utilise gamification, storytelling and other narrative techniques.

A second example of lived experience in an organisational context comes from Chris Lawer, the founder of Umio, who has developed a model of embodied experience which forms the basis of a structured process for understanding, modelling and developing health ecosystems.[79] Having begun his career in insurance marketing, Chris then became interested in customer-centric innovation and transformation, developing and working with various innovation frameworks that put customers' problems and their needs first, and which created value through relationships and systems insight. As Chris told us:

> "For seven years I delivered the Jobs-to-be-Done/Outcome-Driven Innovation method for a diverse body of companies throughout Europe, with the occasional foray in the US, China and South America. Many projects here were with healthcare companies and providers, and it was in these engagements that I began to see not only where existing innovation and design methods were coming up short, but also new possibilities to rethink our approaches for addressing disease and illness and for health."

Umio has developed a transdisciplinary framework, the Health Ecosystem Value Design® (HEVD), whose aim is to advance the health and social care sciences. The purpose was to develop an experience ecosystem of health, disease and illness based on lived experience, rather than more typical outcome-focused clinical research and technology-level solutions. For this reason, we were interested in exploring Chris's motivations for creating the HEVD and to hear him explain what he felt was missing from other frameworks and methodologies:

> "Umio and HEVD came about from personal experience and frustration with prevailing design and innovation thinking and methods in health and care. Despite sustained gains in material wealth, the health of many advanced nations is characterised by increasing prevalence of chronic disease, rising

mental illness, diminishing quality of life and widening inequalities and disparities. Consider chronic pain for example. In most western nations, around 40% of the adult population are suffering from chronic or persistent pain (defined as pain lasting for longer than three months). Whilst the pharmaceutical industry makes billions in pain-alleviating drugs, introducing increasingly stronger and more addictive varieties (with many negative social consequences), we still cannot explain the factors producing adult pain, many of which are beyond the body or fall outside of biomedical explanations alone."

The framework reflects Chris' preoccupations with the manner in which patterns and problems of worsening health, widening inequality, growing disease burden and declining life quality/expectancy are occurring. HEVD seeks to overcome the current limitations in both our methods for understanding these problems and in the effectiveness of our efforts to address them:

"Given that the word 'health' is derived from the Old English words *hal* or *hale* meaning wholeness or whole, the first important task of any health creation framework is to develop a model of wholeness as well as unified lived experience within health. To be whole, such a model must afford the means to identify all the elements that constitute lived experiences with health. To be unified, it must help us see how these elements interact to originate, emerge and variously repeat lived experiences both individually and collectively."

The HEVD framework is systemic in that it identifies the way in which lived experiences with health, disease and illness are formed from individual and multiplicities of *affects*—sensations, feeling states and impressions (sensed in psychological time)—that mark a change within an existing, or a transition to, another experiential state, as well as affective capacities. Because lived experience within this framework is understood as being *whole*, it opens up entirely new ways of thinking about the problem space, thereby allowing us to discover radically different forms of systemic solution. The framework provides a structured way to enter into the lived experience of those people being researched and the problem being studied, while locating the findings in a formally defined ontology, something which many design thinking projects formally define.

A structured ontology allows a designer to construct hypotheses within an expert domain of knowledge which can be scientifically tested, thereby providing insights which can complement the exploratory stages of ideation and co-creation sessions. While experience is a fundamental aspect of all design, it is rare to find the dynamic dimension of wholeness within our lived experience explicitly articulated in the specification of many design thinking and user-centred projects. As Chris explains, the ontology and framework of HEVD can be applied to any context of human experience:

> "For those working with advanced technology and services, the primary lesson is to see a new conception of value that goes beyond transactional, use and service-dominant logic based on exchange. By framing contexts of lived experience, technology and service designers can work within wider, more holistic and open frames of insight and perspective that afford novel trajectories and possibilities for value creation."

Good design is always the result of the appreciation, combination and integration of art, science and technology. Exploring lived experience reminds us that some of the best designers are those who have mastered the art of intuitive understanding. So ultimately this is the aim of design thinking: developing better solutions through understanding the human condition in all its dimensions, principally life as it is experienced in all its livingness.

When we take the time to enter into lived experience and explore systems from the perspective of wholeness, we begin to connect with that which we are designing, developing and deploying in newly empathic ways, revealing to us qualities, impacts and behaviours which may have otherwise remained hidden. In the next chapter we will present our Deep Tech Discovery approach which deepens design practices systemically by integrating and aligning value propositions, agile strategy, lived experience and domain ontologies.

Executive Summary

→ The Holonomics Approach acknowledges that our minds have a natural tendency to interpret the world through a series of filters, frames and biases. These filters are part of our mental models, and they inform our paradigms and how we think, feel and behave.

→ We live in a world that is increasingly complex and interconnected, but we are often not fully aware of how our perception of the world is influenced by our cultural conditioning and our different ways of knowing.

→ Balanced Scorecard is a systemic tool which facilitates the implementation of a strategy. It is a framework which enables organisations to develop agility in the short and long term. The main purpose of the strategy map is to provide a dynamic and living representation of the strategy.

→ Balanced Scorecard is a way of helping an organisation to develop an agile and living systems approach to strategy by linking and integrating the core value proposition into strategy via the strategy map, thereby ensuring that the strategic drivers for change, value proposition, goals, OKRs, indicators and projects are all aligned.

→ Phenomenology is the study of how we experience things. One of its main concepts, lived experience, is a useful way to describe the way in which we experience the world. It is not only relevant to the study of human experience, but also to the way in which we design and develop our technological systems. The HEVD framework, developed by UMIO, is a way of thinking about health and social care based on lived experience.

4

The Logic and Architecture of Deep Tech Platforms

DEEP TECH ECOSYSTEM FORCES

The world's billionaires added USD 3.5 trillion to their wealth in 2020, the equivalent of the gross domestic product (GDP) of Germany, taking their total wealth to USD 14.7 trillion, a massive concentration of economic power.[80] When looking at the five wealthiest individuals globally, the Hurun Global Rich List showed that Tesla's Elon Musk added USD 151 billion to his wealth, becoming the richest man in the world for the first time, with USD 197 billion in net worth. Amazon.com boss Jeff Bezos was in second place with USD 189 billion in net worth, and Bernard Arnault, chief executive of LVMH Moët Hennessy Louis Vuitton, the world's largest luxury-goods company, ranked third globally with a net worth of USD 114 billion. Bill Gates (Microsoft) ranked fourth, and Mark Zuckerberg (Facebook) ranked fifth.

In 2020, during the Covid-19 crisis, China created 259 billionaires, more than the rest of the world combined. This was a result of a booming stock market and new company listings. Taking China's economy as a whole, the country was the only major world economy to experience growth, with GDP up by 2.3 per cent. In comparison, the US shrank by 3.7 per cent, Germany was down 5 per cent, and the UK down by 11 per cent.[81]

In his discussion of the findings, Hurun Report chairman and chief researcher Rupert Hoogewerf observed that, "We are currently right in the heart of a new industrial revolution, with the ABCDEs—that is AI, blockchain, cloud, data and e-commerce—creating new opportunities for entrepreneurs and leading to a concentration of wealth and economic power on a scale never seen before. The world's billionaires now have USD 14 trillion of wealth between them, more than the GDP of China last year".[82]

As we explored in chapter one, businesses with platform-based business models now dominate the global economy. This rapid digital and technological transformation has generated a wave of disruption, meaning that we now need to understand economics in a new way. Despite their impact, however, there is still widespread misunderstanding about platforms and their relation to economic and business models. Many people still understand platforms from the perspective of physical business operating models and pre-platform economics.

Mark Knickrehm, Bruno Berthon and Paul Daugherty provide a functional definition of the digital economy:

> "The digital economy is the share of total economic output derived from a number of broad 'digital' inputs. These digital inputs include digital skills, digital equipment (hardware, software and communications equipment) and the intermediate digital goods and services used in production. Such broad measures reflect the foundations of the digital economy."[83]

Typically, core technological elements in definitions of the digital economy include blockchain technologies, automation and robotics, 3D printing, the internet of things, artificial intelligence, data analytics, cloud computing and 5G and high-speed networks. Other more encompassing definitions also include developments in the life sciences such as genetic modification, nanotechnology, quantum computing and new materials. But what is missing from these definitions is the essential role that *platforms* play in the digital economy, how they function and how they generate, amplify and sustain value.

The digital economy operates under a different logic to traditional economics as a result of the technical architectures of digital organisations, the new offers and services that platforms are enabling and their context within the new economy. As we have seen, the dominance of the United States and China in platform-based enterprises means that they are the most prepared countries for the forthcoming wave of technological disruption because of their understanding of the underlying logic of the digital economy.

Seven new drivers now define the rules of the game in the digital economy. These are:

i.   Exponential network effects
ii. High levels of access to risk investment capital
iii. Low levels of market regulation
iv. Low barriers to entry
v.   Marginal costs of scaling
vi. Immediate global access
vii. Widespread open source and low-cost access to technology innovations

Some factors put a hard limit on platform growth and market leadership. These are:

i.   Clearness of leadership vision
ii. The pool of available human talent
iii. Rate and speed of innovation
iv. Maturity and quality of organisational relations
v.   Responsiveness of corporate change to challenges

The economic, business and human drivers all need to be present to enable an economy to achieve digital maturity. So for example as soon as a new and powerful value proposition is available, new market entrants and substitute products and services can enter the global market immediately and spread rapidly due to exponential network effects and the absence of international frontiers. This new digital dynamic has reduced the relevance of Porter's traditional Five Forces model of competition,[84] which if utilised rigidly can potentially lead to a constant fear of digital disruption in organisations.

Given how digital economies and platforms are inextricably interwoven, we need to understand how digital technologies, services and skills are rapidly expanding across whole economies. Our Deep Tech approach therefore takes an expanded perspective by considering the ethical and moral implications of these new digital drivers.

When levels of market regulation are low, businesses without ethics can prosper without sufficient checks and balances. For this reason, the presence of universal human values in the digital economy is as essential as they are in individual organisations. Human values ensure that all people in the new economy are valued, not just those few with specific advanced technological knowledge and understanding. They also guide which innovations should be investigated, financed, developed and amplified.

To live Deep Tech is to remodel our traditional conceptions of individual enterprises competing for limited resources. When we develop an ecosystem level view of Deep Tech, we shift from a focus on outside forces impacting on a self-contained and bounded organisation to a view of how purpose and value propositions can be accomplished through waves of value amplification (Figure 4.1).

Within a Deep Tech ecosystem, organisations do not lose their individual identities. Their aim is to act in a manner that fully articulates the greater purpose and objectives of that ecosystem. For this reason, our schematic considers forces as amplifying waves, starting with a consideration of the internal resources available to an organisation. These are drawn upon to enable a secondary wave of Deep Tech innovation in which the value proposition is elevated, backbones are developed and platforms are scaled. Once these enabling processes and structures are in place, the organisation can then amplify its impact through systemic relationships, networked business models and collective mastery, enabling leaders to transform their organisations, both digitally and culturally, in an integrated manner.

PLATFORM ELEVATION, SCALING AND AMPLIFICATION

Knickrehm, Berthon and Daugherty explained the digital economy as "the share of total economic output derived from a number of broad 'digital' inputs".[85] Deloitte offers an alternative explanation:

> "The digital economy is the economic activity that results from billions of everyday online connections among people, businesses, devices, data, and processes. The backbone of the digital economy is hyper-connectivity which means the growing interconnectedness of people, organisations and machines that results from the internet, mobile technology and the internet of things (IoT). The digital economy is taking shape and undermining conventional notions about how businesses are structured; how firms interact; and how consumers obtain services, information, and goods."[86]

FIGURE 4.1 Deep Tech Ecosystem Forces

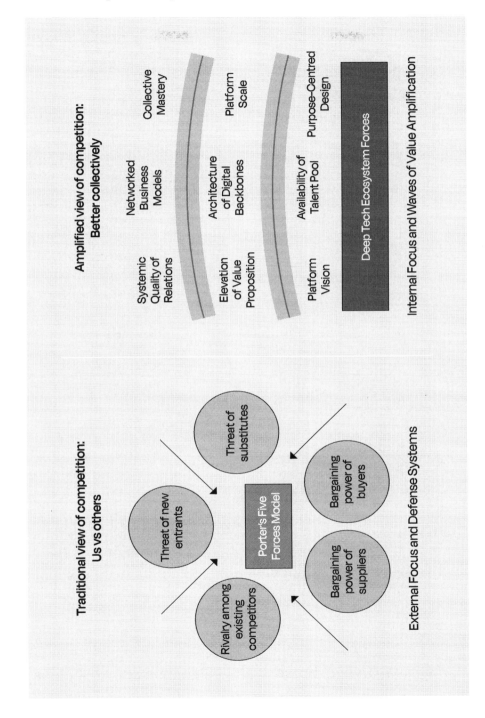

In contrast to these functional definitions of the digital economy, we wanted to provide a more profound explanation of Deep Tech and the digital economy that could speak emotionally, spiritually and economically. Instead of a description consisting simply of quantified inputs and outputs, we feel that it is now time to define the digital economy in a manner that recognises both our human and planetary living ecosystems.

The New 4Ps can help us evolve towards a new conception of the digital economy guided by universal human values and an expanded form of consciousness. We need to understand the dynamic qualities of this emerging digital economy, taking into account both the complex foundational architectures of platforms and quality of life and ecological indicators.

The ecological impact of our use of technology is not just due to the extractive industries mining rare minerals. As Clearfox noted in their report on email pollution: "If the Internet were a country, it would be the 6th biggest polluter in the world. Promotional emails are responsible for two million tons of carbon dioxide (CO_2) emissions annually in the United Kingdom".[87] Websites can also cause pollution, a negative ecological impact which can be reduced through designing more sustainable browsing experiences. In February 2021, Volkswagen, for example, launched their Carbon-Neutral Net, an online redesign to reduce the brand's digital carbon footprint. Volkswagen was able to lower the amount of CO_2 generated by browsing significantly. Their site produced an average of 0.022 grams of CO_2 per page view, in comparison to an average website which produces 1.76 grams of CO_2 per page view.[88]

At a fundamental level, any platform, be it physical or digital, elevates. Our conception of Deep Tech platforms within the digital economy takes into account the perspectives of purpose, people and the planet. For this reason, we define platforms as a mentality, an architecture and enterprise strategy which integrates human and digital dimensions:

Platforms are an open, flexible and extensible set of digital interactions, services and human networks that elevate, scale and amplify value in the digital economy.

We use the word *elevation* in relation to the lifting of a concept to a higher level; you transcend what you have done previously and create something far more inclusive. Our conception of Deep Tech is therefore dynamic, consisting of three design *movements*: the *elevation* of value propositions, *scaling* through technical backbones and platform services, and *amplification* through new waves of innovation (Figure 4.2). The three qualitative movements describe the underlying patterns of transformation. Our schematic contrasts with traditional definitions of the digital economy that focus on outcomes rather than impact on people and the regeneration of our planet through purpose-driven activities.

FIGURE 4.2 The Three Movements of Deep Tech

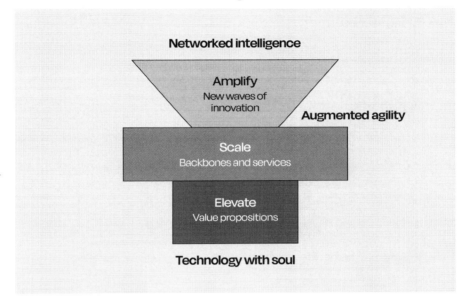

Authentic Deep Tech ecosystems are purpose-driven and focus on the quality of relationships and social, economic and environmental impact through the presence and expression of universal human values. The ability of platforms to scale represents a significant opportunity to raise the quality of life for people. Due to the low marginal cost of scaling, once a value proposition has been elevated, it can then be scaled globally at a minimal cost.

To fully understand how the digital economy has evolved to its present state, it is essential to understand its constituent layers. Figure 4.3 shows the impact that the past three economic crises—the 2000 internet dot-com bubble, the 2008 world financial crisis and the 2020 Covid-19 pandemic—had on the birth of new sectors.

FIGURE 4.3 The Evolution of the Digital Economy

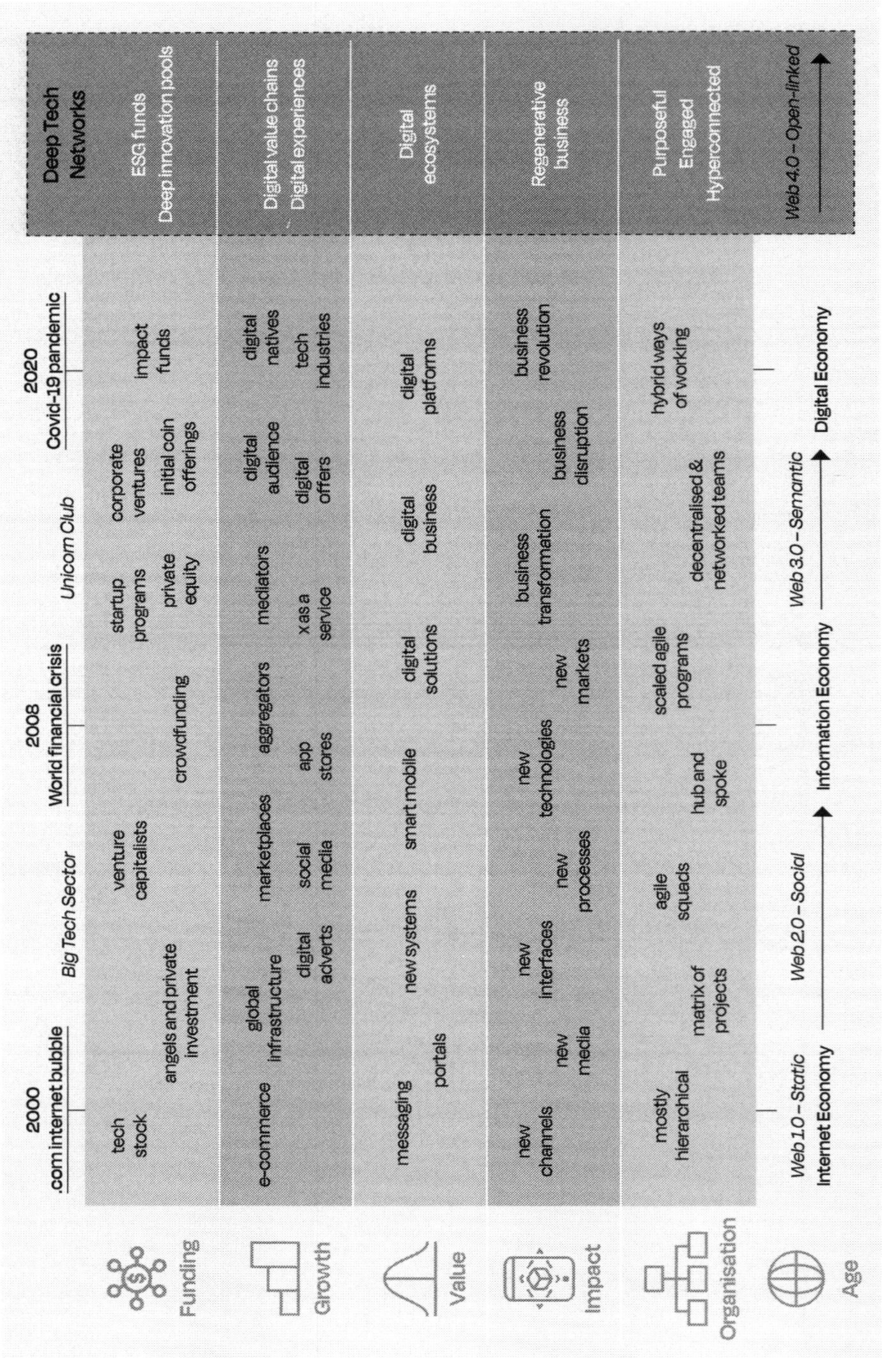

	2000 .com internet bubble	Big Tech Sector	2008 World financial crisis	Unicorn Club	2020 Covid-19 pandemic	Deep Tech Networks
Funding	tech stock; angels and private investment	venture capitalists	crowdfunding	startup programs; private equity; corporate ventures; initial coin offerings	impact funds	ESG funds; Deep innovation pools
Growth	e-commerce; global infrastructure; digital adverts	marketplaces; social media	app stores; aggregators	mediators; x as a service	digital audience; digital offers; digital natives; tech industries	Digital value chains; Digital experiences
Value	messaging; portals; new systems		smart mobile; digital solutions	digital business	digital business; digital platforms	Digital ecosystems
Impact	new channels; new media; new interfaces; new processes		new technologies; new markets	business transformation; business disruption	business revolution	Regenerative business
Organisation	mostly hierarchical; matrix of projects	agile squads; hub and spoke	scaled agile programs	decentralised & networked teams	hybrid ways of working	Purposeful; Engaged; Hyperconnected
Age	Web 1.0 – Static — Internet Economy	Web 2.0 – Social — Information Economy		Web 3.0 – Semantic — Digital Economy		Web 4.0 – Open-linked

Between 2000 and 2008, online portals offering e-commerce transformed into marketplaces. Following this, new business models such as Software as a Service and global mediators such as Uber and Air BnB emerged. The scale and extension of platforms were made possible through their value propositions and the evolution of financial funding mechanisms. Early startups received risk capital through angel and private investment. Once the big-tech sector started to form, the structuring of investment in the digital economy became more sophisticated with the development of large venture capital investment funds. As digital infrastructure reached global mass, a new order of applications was developed, such as Gmail, cloud computing, protocols and standards that are now in use today.

New digital markets emerged, for example, markets as a service (e.g., software as a service, platforms as a service, infrastructure as a service). These new markets created a further impact on businesses in relation to the design of organisational structures and business processes. For example, following the Covid crisis, hybrid management systems are now being created with people partly present in their workplaces and partly remote or working at home. Organisations are now transforming by basing their structures on the logic of platforms. New opportunities are emerging for recruitment, with employees and contractors currently working in any region of the world. The result is hybrid organisations with management systems that are primarily digital and highly fluid.

Fluidity provides an organisation with the ability to react rapidly to changing contexts, mounting and dismounting agile teams as necessary. This fluidity comes from the organisational structure and executive teams having the requisite level of platform vision. Without a clear understanding of platform architectures and their component elements, an organisation will be constantly challenged, never reaching its potential in the digital economy.

As interoperability across digital systems increases, organisations become able to expand their boundaries from value chain collaboration to Deep Tech regenerative ecosystems. The starting point for the development of these initiatives within an amplified organisation is the Deep Tech Discovery process and the elevation of that organisation's core value proposition.

DEEP TECH DISCOVERY AND VALUE PROPOSITION ELEVATION

Design Council is a British independent charity and the United Kingdom government's advisor on design. Their stated vision is: "a world where the role and value of design are recognised as a fundamental creator of value, enabling happier, healthier and safer lives for all. Through the power of design, we make better processes, better products, better places, all of which lead to better performance".[89] In the past, while project teams across Design Council talked about the design process, they didn't have a standard way of presenting this process or a consistent way of managing design projects. With this in mind, Richard Eisermann, Design Council's then Director of Design and Innovation, asked his team how they would describe the design process. The answer which came back was the now-famous double diamond visual representation of the design and innovation process.[90]

FIGURE 4.4 The Double Diamond

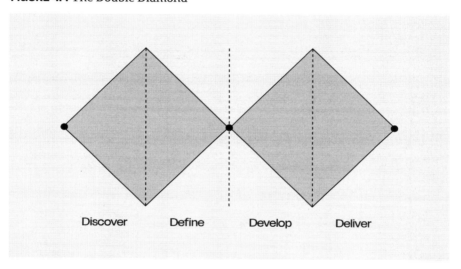

Discover   Define   Develop   Deliver

The power of the double diamond comes from the way it describes the steps taken in any design and innovation project, irrespective of any methods and tools used. While other researchers and design teams had referenced the use of the diamond shape to help describe their methodologies, it would be Design Council who would most fully codify design by mapping out the standard stages. The diamond, therefore, shows four distinct phases:

Discover: The process starts by questioning the challenge and quickly leads to research to identify user needs.
Define: The second phase is to make sense of the findings, understanding how user needs and the problem align. The result is to create a design brief that clearly

defines the challenge based on these insights.

Develop: The third phase concentrates on developing, testing and refining multiple potential solutions.

Deliver: The final phase involves selecting a single solution that works and preparing it for launch.[91]

Today, many businesses now follow the double diamond stages in designing and developing their platform projects and initiatives. The idea is to start with an initial challenge or problem statement. A design team then formulates a definition of the problem to be addressed and ends with a final solution. The diamond shapes represent two different movements of thinking; divergent thinking, which is expansive and exploratory, and convergent thinking, which is analytical and focused on definitions, specifications, and answers. The process is iterative, the main activities being research, learning, prototyping, and testing.

While many new products, services and startup business models have been created and tested using this iterative design cycle, the complexity of Deep Tech platforms means that these processes alone are no longer sufficient for their development and deployment. For this reason, 1STi and Holonomics combined their expertise and innovations across the fields of platform architecture, customer experience design and cultural transformation to develop a new Deep Tech Discovery process. Figure 4.5 shows the main elements and general order of the activities involved (which in reality constitute an iterative and non-linear process).

Our experience in platform design and digital transformation has led to us identifying the following mistakes that executive teams make when structuring complex platform initiatives:

- The organisation does not align design teams with the overall strategy or core value proposition;
- The organisation does not understand the logic of digital economy business models;
- There is an inadequate understanding of how platforms generate value for users, customers and clients;
- There is not sufficient understanding of the technical building blocks of platforms;
- There is confusion around the platform architecture and its boundaries with the underlying technologies and services that support the platform;

FIGURE 4.5 Deep Tech Discovery

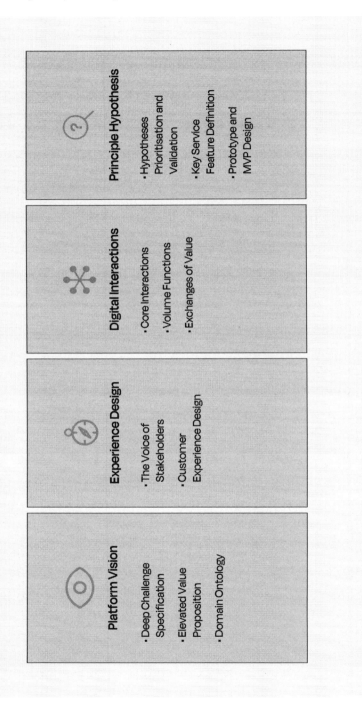

- There are organisation-wide cognitive biases operating that lead to conflicting or limited conceptions of the platform based on people's functions.

With platform design being so complex, the starting point is to instigate a discovery phase of research. The traditional goal for a design thinking processes is to end up with a minimum viable product (MVP), a working prototype of the platform that contains the simplest core feature set that allows it to be deployed. An MVP, therefore, represents the smallest thing that can be built which delivers some form of customer value. It is constructed to obtain feedback from early adopters and determine the strategic direction of further product development. Once this feedback has been received, the MVP can undergo rapid iterations after it has entered a market to reach a more desirable state.[92]

Our Deep Tech Discovery phase has been structured around the need to facilitate a systemic understanding of the mindsets, platform architectures, and conceptual definitions of Deep Tech. We created the process to:

i.   develop enterprise-wide agility through the integration of strategy, value propositions and platform development;
ii.   facilitate an appreciation of the many different mindsets that operate in organisations, for example, the managerial, the entrepreneurial and the visionary;[93]
iii.   demystify the core concepts relating to complex platform architectures;
iv.   expand the concept of discovery from a focus on the voice of the customer to the voice of stakeholders;
v.   align Deep Tech platform architectures with the organisation's digital operating model;
vi.   develop a unified understanding of core concepts across different divisions and teams in an organisation.

This approach to discovery incorporates several new technologies and experience design methodologies into more traditional frameworks and processes such as service design blueprinting and customer journey mapping. We integrate problem specification and ideation activities with educational sessions based on developing organisation-wide alignment around core concepts and definitions. The result is a more agile form of design and development with engaged contributors for all parts of the organisation and the efficient integration of legacy systems into the platform architecture. The enterprise logic that describes business processes and strategy can also be aligned with the functionality and purpose of the platform.

Agility in organisations today is still often only practiced in design teams. When thinking about the core qualities of agile software development, no matter what the methodology (Scrum, Kanban, XP, etc.) there are five core aspects that can be adopted by any department or division. These are value-driven development, the use of visual tools, multi-disciplinary team working, regular short meetings and continual review. As we mentioned in chapter four, a shortcoming of many agile projects is a lack of integration into an organisation's overall strategy, due to a failure in leadership communication and alignment. For this reason, strategy maps with an explicit elevated value proposition are the ideal visual tool to add to agile projects for an organisation to achieve enterprise-wide agility. In this manner, the objectives of each agile team and squad can always be checked against higher-level organisational OKRs and other indicators, meaning that design and development teams automatically acquire strategic consciousness and are able to articulate exactly how their designs will deliver value through meeting organisational goals.

The integration of business and enterprise architectures with Deep Tech architectures begins with developing platform vision. This can be achieved not only through communication and alignment within the Deep Tech Discovery process, but also by integrating semantic alignment into the design process. This is the practice of making different cognitive, data and expert domain models explicit through the development of *ontological domains* (explained in chapter six). The idea is to help organisations make a shift from a technical focus on big data and problem specification on jobs-to-be done, up to a higher level where data and information becomes integrated, networked and able to deliver far more meaningful insights and analysis.

One of the first hurdles to developing platform vision is the conceptual confusion that often exists between digital businesses, systems and platforms. These differing concepts can be best understood by looking at how the digitalisation of business evolved. At the start of the first internet wave in the early 1990s, companies started to build portals that provided new channels to market, powered by the first e-commerce technologies. Online portals such as AOL and CompuServe, and then mobile portals such as British Telecom's Genie Internet, created unified customer experiences by integrating information such as news, travel, weather, sports, and entertainment with the first generation of online shopping services.

As web technologies and digital user experience design practices developed, portals brought new channels, media, interfaces, processes and technologies into the economy. Following this phase, we learned to create new digital systems. A digital system is an integrated set of digital components, service interfaces and computational infrastructure that are highly scalable, available and economically efficient. Some examples are customer relationship management (CRM) systems, learning management systems (LMS), and content management systems (CMS).

In the following phase of digitalisation, these systems were integrated to create digital solutions capable of producing or augmenting critical business capabilities. An example is a multi-channel marketing solution that can send a range of messages such as emails, SMS messages and which defines rules, business logic, and market segmentation on communications workflows. So a digital solution contains multiple digital systems and critically impacts on one or more business capabilities.

In contrast to platforms designed for the logic of the digital economy, digital solutions usually have an internal perspective and are based on niche business capabilities. They are always created in a closed manner, meaning they cannot scale and extend to new markets and elevated value propositions. Today, many modern startups are closed digital solutions rather than being built on an open platform logic. However, this does not stop these solutions from being positioned as platforms, resulting in conceptual confusion for leaders who are not fully digitally literate.

This architectural misunderstanding can present significant challenges for businesses that grow through acquisitions. Purchased businesses can often be challenging to integrate into holding companies because their digital systems are not interoperable. Digital solutions can be evolved into platforms through architectural re-engineering, a process which requires the various digital components to be made open for extension, evolution and reconfiguration.

Digital Business: provide deeply innovative, highly flexible and scalable digital offers through a business model that is mostly or entirely digital.

Digital Platforms: open, flexible and extensible set of digital interactions and services.

Deep Tech Ecosystems: go beyond market value to provide regenerative economic value and creativity through Deep Tech platforms and networks of people where universal human values are present.

FIGURE 4.6 The Evolution of Competition

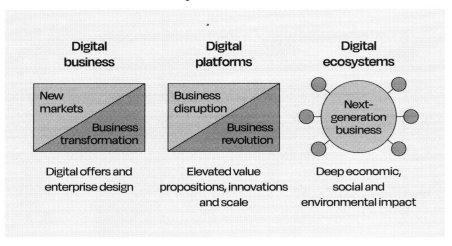

The new competitive digital landscape can be understood with three distinct categories. Figure 4.6 shows the evolution of business transformation through disruptive innovation to the next generation of businesses that drive meaningful economic, social and environmental impact. Platforms are playing a central role in this disruption, one example being MOOCs (massively online open courses) which have disrupted the educational market by providing self-service on-demand educational options that previously did not exist. Commercial educational platforms such as Udemy are both digital businesses and platforms. Udemy's platform's logic enables users to create MOOCs in several different styles and with differing features, such as digital payment options. It allows people to submit their courses and construct interactions and customer journeys, and is also extensible through affiliates and instructor open interfaces (APIs). Its openness allows anyone to submit their content and integrate, extend or customise its platform services and marketplace.

When businesses open the digital services of their platforms, they achieve higher levels of elevation and scale. This is in contrast to Netflix, which at this moment is a closed digital business. They do not allow, for example, user-generated content such as film evaluations. It could easily be possible for Netflix to open its system to become a corporate learning platform with content catalogs, user recommendations engines and streaming for example, or become a platform for a new distributed media group, leveraging their creative studios to produce creative new narratives with the purpose of evolving societal knowledge.

Digital technologies are disrupting traditional industrial sectors in several ways. Amplified organisations are able to think about platforms in a way that is not restricted to individual industries and which facilitates interconnection across differing sectors. An example of this is Ame, a fintech customer loyalty solution developed by the Brazilian wholesaler Americanas. Their introduction includes the observation that every team member has strategic consciousness:

> "The world has changed, so why do we use our money in the same way? Ame is a fintech created to simplify and revolutionise the way people relate to money. This purpose guides us every day. We were born as a digital account, but we are growing to become an essential financial platform in people's lives. We work in squads, with multifunctional and multifaceted teams, to deliver functionalities in an agile and continuous way. Here everyone is an 'owner of the business' participating in the definition of our strategy and technology."[94]

Our Deep Tech approach to platform design classifies cross-sectoral digitalisation in three different ways:

1. **Expansion of a product or service into other sectors,** e.g., a fintech creating credit solutions for specific industries by offering financial credit, consultancy and access to markets as a single packaged service.
2. **Expansion of the market,** e.g., a wholesaler such as Ame creating a financial loyalty product that can be used for any purchase a customer makes, allowing them to receive points for wholesale purchases or cashback payments into their accounts.
3. **Elevation of the value proposition**, e.g., an educational organisation expanding from brick-and-mortar schools and colleges to creating an educational platform that offers open distance-learning courses.

The extension of products or services into other industry sectors and the expansion of markets are ways for an organisation to grow its business. Our conception of Deep Tech is multifaceted, focusing on purpose-centred design, a process we describe in chapter six. While many companies articulate how they provide value to customers through value propositions, Deep Tech Discovery starts with a strategic process we call Value Proposition Elevation. Figure 5.5 shows our framework with the key elements that enable this elevation.

The first step is to describe an organisation's current core value proposition. It is then analysed and then elevated through the lenses of i) planetary challenges, ii) the organisation's values and iii) its future-fit vision. The process of elevating a platform's value proposition also contributes to an organisation's wider digital evolution initiatives, for example, strategic initiatives, digital products/services, digital solutions and advanced technologies.

FIGURE 4.7 Value Proposition Elevation

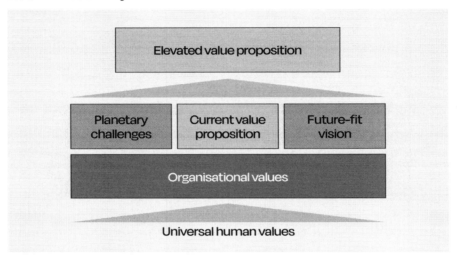

The process of value proposition elevation integrates organisational values with an organisation's strategy and platform value proposition. Therefore, the framework utilises existing elements and assets within an organisation to re-think the nature of the platform value proposition. The strategic purpose of the technology which the organisation develops comes directly from the values of the organisation and regenerative and sustainable frameworks such as the Future-Fit Benchmark.[95]

The term 'future-fit' was coined by Geoff Kendall, CEO and Co-Founder of the Future-Fit Foundation, after realising there was no reliable way to measure how sustainable a company is now and how much more it needs to do. Wanting to fix this, in 2014 he set up the Future-Fit Foundation with the aim of helping organisations make the transition to a future-fit society, one which "protects the possibility that humans and other life will flourish on Earth forever, by being environmentally restorative, socially just and economically inclusive."[96]

This led to Kendall and his colleagues developing the Future-Fit Benchmark, a new form of benchmark which has the following three characteristics:

i. A set of system principles that collectively describe how society can flourish within the physical limits of our finite planet;
ii. A set of future-fit goals that every company must reach by mapping the system principles onto business activities;
iii. Key performance indicators (KPIs) that measure how far away any company is from reaching the future-fit goals.[97]

The core underlying principle of the benchmark is that a future-fit company generates net-positive economic, social, and environmental value. So rather than merely focusing on today's best practice, organisations must measure the gap between where they are now and where they need to be. Any initiative to elevate a value proposition must therefore include the fundamental principle of the Future-Fit Benchmark which states that, "being 'least bad' among peers is not good enough: to thrive, a business must find new ways to create value which delivers environmental, social and financial success".[98]

To truly amplify an organisation, this future-fit vision must be fully coherent and integrated with the organisation's values. Our Elevated Value Proposition framework helps people across the organisation make the links between values, culture, strategy and value proposition explicit. Table 4.1 provides three different examples of elevations of baseline value propositions.

The examples demonstrate how baseline value propositions are often phrased in more functional terminology, focusing on the underlying business model rather than the higher-level purpose. The process of elevation and the integration of organisational values and future-fit vision starts in the preliminary stage of Deep Tech Discovery, with dialogue and ideation sessions structured around the New 4Ps. The result is an engaging and inspirational value proposition that can help to amplify the organisation's impact and facilitate the transition into the digital economy.

This digital transformation can only be achieved by those organisations who understand the relationship between platforms, the data value chain and the interoperable systems and solutions upon which platforms are built. Interoperable systems, constructed using international standards and protocols, enable platforms to expand and offer new and rapidly scalable services. They are the mechanisms that create digital capabilities and the foundation for the provision of platform-specific services.

TABLE 4.1 Elevated Value Propositions

Value Proposition	Organisational Values	Future-Fit Vision	Elevated Value Proposition
Digital health solution for the co-ordination of medical care team available 24/7 Private health business model	Collaboration Integrity Systemic solutions	New health ontologies based on the lived experience of patients and a systemic view of medical care	**Caring Communities** Health ecosystems which authentically integrate the practices of health professionals, private health care providers, prevention and care therapists, schools and businesses
New Digital Learning Experience Platform Tuition-fee business model	Innovation Collective impact Unique experiences	Open knowledge and shared construction of learning based on real-world challenges	**Open Education** Business models for remuneration of participation and personal evolution in open projects in companies
Updating of critical applications and platform integrations in retail e-commerce Efficiency-based business models	Dynamism Proximity to the customer Negotiation skills	Circular economy supply chain development	**Impact Commerce** The issuing of regenerative credit tokens and currencies to suppliers of best ecological, social and governance practices

It is essential to understand platforms regarding their services and the core digital capabilities that enable those services. Collectively they are referred to as backbones which package interoperable core services together and structure business capabilities. Backbones are of central importance to the digital economy since they form the cohesive foundations on which platforms are built. While only a minority of digital businesses have implemented operational backbones, research from MIT suggests that those who do achieve 2.5x more agility and are 1.4x more innovative.[99]

When platforms are built flexibly, they can be opened up with extensions to create new solutions created by external partners. It is this aspect that leads to the evolution of platforms into digital ecosystems. Today, for example, Instagram is not just a platform. There is an entire ecosystem of solutions that utilise the platform's functionalities.

FIGURE 4.8 Digital Backbones

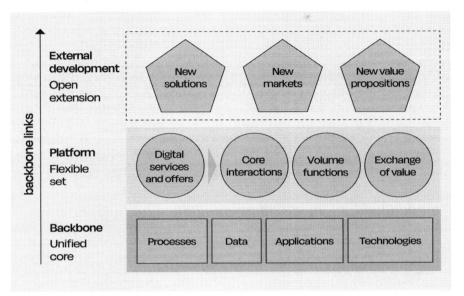

Platforms need to be both flexible and extensible at the same time. To grow, the platform has to be rapidly customisable and have the ability to extend into new markets and sectors. Platform flexibility and extensibility are characterised through five core dimensions:

1. Value Proposition Elevation: Platforms elevate the concept of value created by business capabilities, digital offers and customer experiences.

2. Scalable Services: Scaling enables rapid experimentation and growth in new markets, products/services and innovative business models.

3. Network Effects: Network effects facilitate the creation and amplification of new waves of value through open models.

4. Backbone Stability: Digital backbones provide the foundation of platforms and guarantee a strong nucleus of interoperability, integrity and security for digital services.

5. Quality of Interactions: These refer to the different forms of interactions that users have with platforms: core interactions, volume functions and exchanges of value.

When an organisation decides to take the first step into platform-based business models, expensive and time-consuming mistakes can be made if there is confusion between the demarcation of the digital backbone and the digital services provided by the platform. Any executive team responsible for determining the scope and requirements of a new platform must articulate and document the different ways users interact with the platform. Our Deep Tech Discovery process characterises these platform interactions as follows:

1. Core interactions

All platforms have a range of services that they offer. They manage to grow by having relatively simple fundamental interactions which are carefully designed to reinforce the core value proposition. Facebook's key interactions are liking, sharing, and visualising content on the timeline. WhatsApp's are sending a short message, image or archive.

2. Volume functions

Volume functions are those which allow the platform to increase the number of people who use it. Facebook allows people to add friends and see friends of friends. WhatsApp reads the contacts in your smartphone. Instagram has influencers who create volume due to people wanting to be inspired and follow the lives of celebrities.

3. Exchanges of value

The exchange of value sustains the business model of the platform. For example, Facebook has advertising, WhatsApp maintains the control of communication both inside Facebook and as a standalone app, and WeChat orchestrates an industry of applications and payments.

The exchange of value in platforms has previously been a hidden aspect of platforms and their applications. Users are not often aware of the nature of the exchange of value that sustains expansion and growth. In 2018, Dima Yarovinsky, an artist and user experience designer shocked visitors when his *I Agree* project was showcased in the US at the Visualizing Knowledge exhibition, demonstrating just how immensely long the terms and conditions are for smart phone apps when printed out.[100] He introduced his project at the event in the following way:

> "I took the content of the 'terms of service' of the leading online services that we use on a daily basis (including Facebook, Snapchat, Instagram, Tinder, etc.) and printed them on a standard A4 wide scroll with a standard legal contract font size and type. After printing these so-called terms, I hanged the scrolls in the gallery at the academy, added the number of words and the time it takes to read each scroll on the floor. My main goal was to emphasise how small and helpless we are against these giant corporates."[101]

Good platform design is based on an expansion of the functional perspective in order to arrive at a deeper intentional dimension. The objective is to shift from the widely used basic formula which focuses on volume of users and data generated to continuous waves of authentic value amplification. This can be achieved when:

- Platform interactions reinforce the elevated value proposition
- Platform services are flexible, extensible and inspired by a clear platform vision
- The digital backbone creates strong interoperability between operational value chains and platform services

The final stage of Deep Tech Discovery is the development of a set of platform hypotheses. Our process makes explicit the need for hypotheses to include the voice of significant stakeholders, and not just the voice of the customer. They are then prioritised and evaluated by designing and developing a prototype, technological proof of concept, experiment or minimum viable product. The architecture is also minimal and focused on testing individual digital services, sets of platform interactions, technical viability and platform concepts.

As soon as this initial testing demonstrates that the value proposition is viable and scalable, it is then possible to begin articulating a future-fit vision which is the basis for developing an 'intentional architecture' (explained in chapter five). User testing needs to explore people's immediate needs and how the platform services will serve future needs and aspirations. Once these are understood, the articulation of the platform can start to evolve towards the intentional architecture.

Capturing the scale and power of Deep Tech platforms through their elevated value propositions, networked business models and ecosystem forces represents a significant opportunity for organisations in the digital economy. For this to happen, business leaders need to free their thinking from a closed perspective based only on short-term financial results which come from technology-centric developments and which can reinforce social inequalities in our society. Thinking more deeply about platform architecture and design results in more sustainable and networked models of economic growth, enabling companies to be exemplars of a movement that amplifies wellbeing, reduces inequality through the defence of human rights and which places more focus on our most profound challenges.

Executive Summary

→ A new digital economy is being created and transforming the way we think about value creation in business and society. We need to understand how Deep Tech is creating new business and economic models for the future.

→ Deep Tech is the next phase of the digital economy; a new form of innovation that is more inclusive, purpose-driven and regenerative.

→ Platforms represent the next generation of business models. They are the next step in the evolution of competition. The design of Deep Tech platforms is a complex process that requires the integration of many different mindsets and skillsets.

→ The design and development of Deep Tech platforms is a complex and highly iterative process. The most successful projects are those that are aligned with the organisation's overall strategy, value proposition and digital operating model. Agile projects can be adopted by any department or division within an organisation, but an organisation as a whole still needs a unifying strategy map that contains the elevated value proposition of the organisation.

→ The design of Deep Tech platforms is a process of creating an open, extensible and highly networked digital architecture. It is a set of digital interactions and services that elevate, scale and amplify value in the digital economy.

→ Deep Tech Discovery is a systematic approach to the challenge of integrating and aligning value propositions, agile strategy, lived experience and domain ontologies to unlock new opportunities for value creation. It is based on the premise that the most powerful platform business models are based on an elevated value proposition, a networked business model and ecosystem forces.

5

Designing and Scaling Deep Tech Platforms

THE ARCHITECTURE OF DIGITAL TRANSFORMATION

Organisations achieve scale and elevation through designing and implementing complex Deep Tech platform architectures. As we saw, however, in chapter four, it is still the case today that organisations are facing the challenge of limitations in the availability of talent, which limits their ability to play a leading role in the digital economy. The human dimension of digital transformation can result in many different inhibitors acting together to create further barriers to an organisation being able to amplify itself. For this reason, in this chapter we will demonstrate exactly what these inhibitors are, how they operate, and how leaders can manage them, once they have been identified and understood.

While the term 'digital transformation' has often been defined in a number of ways and sometimes used ambiguously, we define it as the shift in the way an organisation delivers value through the implementation of digital business models, digital operating models and digital platforms. Since the ultimate goal is one of strategic business transformation, digital transformation initiatives should always be accompanied by cultural transformation. This leads to the implementation of optimised digital operating models that are aligned with both enterprise and digital architectures, making the expansion and scaling of the company possible through people who are empowered, engaged and who have a strategic understanding of Deep Tech platforms and the elevated value proposition.

Expansion and scaling are enabled through the definition of digital platform capabilities (Figure 5.1). Our Deep Tech platform design methodology structures these capabilities by configuring them in four fundamental layers. The direction of digital transformation always starts with the definition of the inner layer of core value proposition and then building outwards with the platform services, growth capabilities and finally, the platform extension points. Implementing digital transformation in this manner enables organisations to amplify their purpose, increase their competitiveness and achieve leadership positions in the digital economy.

FIGURE 5.1 Digital Platform Capabilities

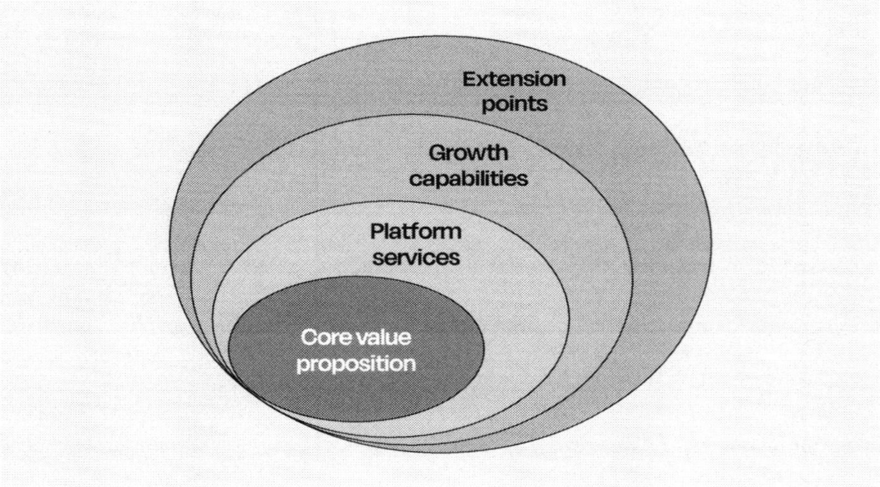

The purpose of a platform is articulated through its core value proposition. For example, the value proposition of Facebook is to be a global social network that gets close to communities and gives a voice to all people. Instagram's core value proposition is to allow people to share moments from their daily lives. Once a core value proposition has been developed and the core interactions articulated, it is then possible to identify those platform services that deliver the promised value. For example, Facebook has privacy services, groups and advertising.

Organisations that do not possess platform vision do not differentiate between a platform's core value proposition and the services that the platform offers. Platforms should always be built by first defining this core value proposition before its services. It is the services that make possible and amplify the core value proposition and not the other way around.

Growth capabilities are a standard layer that allow platform services to be scaled and converted into revenue streams. One reason for defining these capabilities as a separate layer is that many inspiring value propositions do not reach a massive scale despite their technical and market viability due to the absence of the specification of platform architecture growth capabilities. This layer is particularly suitable for the accelerated integration of vendor frameworks, solutions and marketing platforms.

An example growth capability is multi-channel communication which can be located across a range of platforms. A second example is multi-factor authentication which provides users with a sense of protection when interacting with a platform. Personalisation and recommendation services such as suggesting potential friends or user behaviour analytics are always built as a layer above the platform services that enable a growing platform user base and service engagement.

The final layer of a platform's capabilities is its extension points. These allow partners and third-party developers to access and utilise a platform's services and growth capabilities through the deployment of open interfaces. These open interfaces need to have well-designed connections with the growth capabilities and platform services. Without them the platform will always remain constricted with limited possibilities to scale and expand.

Figure 5.2 shows some common growth capabilities in operation in platforms today. These are located within the platform services layer and within the context of the main associated platform architectural elements with which they interconnect.

The first layer relates to customer care in the form of the registration, management and retention of users on the platform. Unified account management allows people to use the same account, such as a Google account, across multiple platforms. Multi-factor authentication contributes to growth by enabling many different methods for automatically logging in to a platform. Facebook manages this form of authentication for example by always being logged in to both a user's phone and their computer's web browser. This enables Facebook to connect the phone number with that specific browser. If an attempt is made to log in via a browser which has never been used before with Facebook, a message will be sent to the phone to check that it is the authorised person logging in, rather than being an attempt to hack in to the account. This allows the platform to remain open continually while still providing a degree of security for users.

FIGURE 5.2 Growth Capabilities Architecture

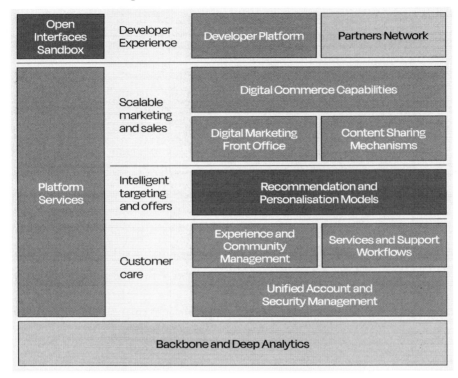

Additional capabilities in this layer relate to customer engagement. This includes the management of user communities, social reputation management and customer services. Social reputation and sharing are capabilities which allow users to manage negative comments or reviews and help build brands with transparency.

The second layer refers to intelligent targeting and offers. This includes personalisation and recommendation models embedded into a platform's key transaction interfaces and content workflows. This intelligence layer enables personalisation at scale and ensures that people receive offers and content specific to their profiles and needs. Several personalisation and recommendation models are currently available based on user behaviour, personal data and clustering algorithms.

5 · DESIGNING AND SCALING DEEP TECH PLATFORMS

The third layer relates to scalable digital marketing and sales. Key messages, co-created content, special offers and digital brand assets are managed through the integration across different channels such as messaging, portals, commerce, social media, advertising and marketplaces. Users are therefore able to receive messages and content which are unified across every point of contact. Content networks, for example, have the ability to leverage digital audience channels on social media channels such as Instagram or Youtube by providing expanded analyses on platform usage on specific groups. Understanding the organic language of digital influencers and the way in which people collaborate in the digital space can generate many ideas in how to create new forms of platform value and how to enhance the platform's roadmap. For this to happen it is essential to take the challenges and regulations of advertising, user privacy and data protection into account.

Digital commerce solutions need be designed from the perspective of platform fluidity. This is achieved in practice by designing fit-for-purpose next-generation order and payments services which are able to accommodate every form of transaction and operate in as many channels as possible. Examples are real-time servicing (immediate online consultancy for entrepreneurs, tailored masterclasses for the student or specific groups, and customised digital experiences for a family); on demand automated shopping (devices such as refrigerators choosing to buy certain quantities of products according to pre-determined parameters such as dietary needs of a family); and live commerce (potential buyers interacting online through direct conversations with sellers).

While user experience is now a common design practice, the developers who build services based on a platform's capabilities are a community whose requirements are often not explicitly taken into account. For this reason, the developer experience layer sits on top of the growth capabilities layer. From a technical perspective, this architectural block consists of open interfaces that allow developers to extend the platform. Developer experience can also be thought of as a user experience design practice that considers how external developers need to understand and think about the models and functionality of a platform. This community therefore requires access to test services and technical support to help them learn how to exploit the platform capabilities to their fullest.

A platform's growth capabilities are built on top of the backbone and the deep analytics layer (Figure 5.3). Large-scale analytical capabilities enable the growth and evolution of the platform and its services. They do this by integrating data

FIGURE 5.3 Deep Analytics

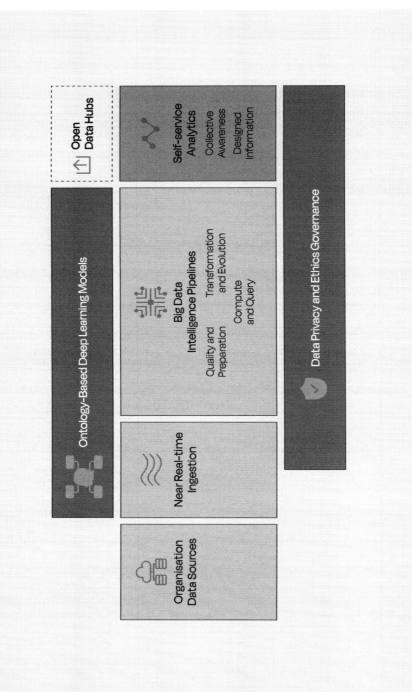

streams from different sources in near real-time, providing the capacity to understand a user's profile and behaviour. The use of ontology-based deep learning models (explained in more detail in chapter six) means that user data can be placed into a wider semantic context which understands their journey throughout the platform, thereby allowing the platform to make intelligent inferences about the intentions of both individual users and groups. Deep analytics integrates all sources of data generated by the platform together with open data sets to support growth capabilities by creating an intelligence layer for every service on the platform.

Deep Analytics must be operated within an organisation's frameworks for data privacy and ethics governance. These define the policies and verification mechanisms to support the development of analytical and deep learning models in a manner that is as unbiased and as fair as possible.

The backbone, introduced in the previous chapter, provides the underlying foundational layer on which the platform is built. Continuous and fast-paced innovations and digital offers are strongly dependent on dynamic operational models and capabilities which require a unified foundation of core processes, data, applications and technologies. If we wish to develop platforms with scalable and flexible services, we need a highly unified nucleus, which is the backbone.

A well-designed backbone ensures that the platform services and the customer experience have structural integrity and are interoperable across the entire architecture. So for example, a well-designed platform will have one single user model, which all services reference. This means that new services which are launched, such as a payment service, always references the single user profile instead of a separate user profile elsewhere.

Three particular backbone capabilities contribute to the growth of the platform:

1. Core data and transaction models

The core data and transaction models define the principle ways in which an organisation's platform-based business model generates revenue through data modelling of main user interactions. For example, Facebook is based on a graph that models core connections between people. Twitter has a data model for micro-blogging. The backbone contains a core domain model for data which represents the structure of the value proposition. It is imperative to design a high-quality data model that can fully reflect the logic of business models and value propositions.

Some organisations do not take the time to design an explicit domain model or do not understand the need for them, choosing instead to focus on the design of the platform services. This is an error since it is the quality of the description of the core data model that enables the platform to function optimally and have the flexibility to support a wide range of services. Many of the problems that arise when different organisations merge or have their systems integrated result from core domain models either not having been defined or not being compatible. For this reason, organisations require expertise in computational ontologies, which we explain in detail in chapter six.

2. Autonomous operations infrastructure

Platforms need to scale internationally and across multiple markets and industries. The level of complexity in their architectures means that platforms need to have a degree of autonomy related to self-healing. When excessive use of resources has been identified, this degree of autonomy enables a platform to enter into a dynamic mode of operation that enables it to cope with this additional capacity, allowing it to recuperate from this extreme operational state. Platforms are also able to self-repair when core resources fail for some reason. When this happens, the platform automatically makes use of previously redundant resources. So a platform's autonomy allows it to repair and recover intelligently and scale dynamically when necessary.

3. Event workflows

The scale and expansion of platforms have resulted in extremely complex challenges relating to how they operate and how platform events are processed through the digital operating model of a company. For this reason, platforms are managed operationally through event workflows, which enable the choreography of services, thereby maintaining high levels of co-ordination across services and applications. Example events are adding an item for sale on eBay, creating an account and adding a product to a shopping cart. Because many different parts of a platform (service domains) may be interested in these events, they must be choreographed in order to remain synchronised. This complex choreography is achieved by connecting all of the different services that require access to the events via an event stream hub (Figure 5.4).

In the 1990s, monolithic software systems that lacked a structured architecture and developed without the technique of technology decoupling could often result

FIGURE 5.4 Service Choreography

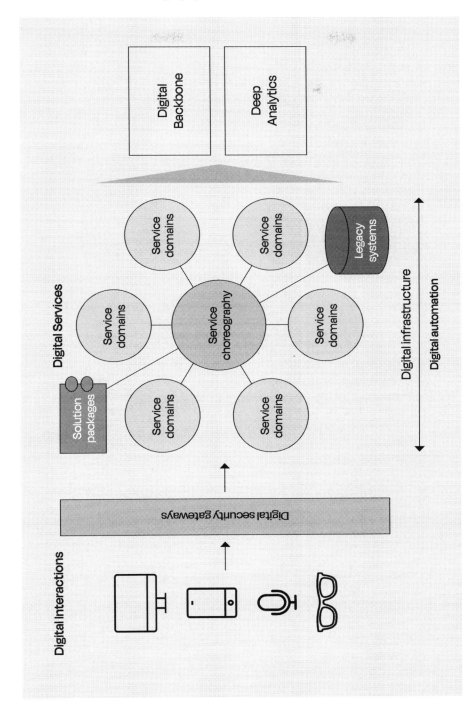

FIGURE 5.5 Deep Tech Platform Lifecycle

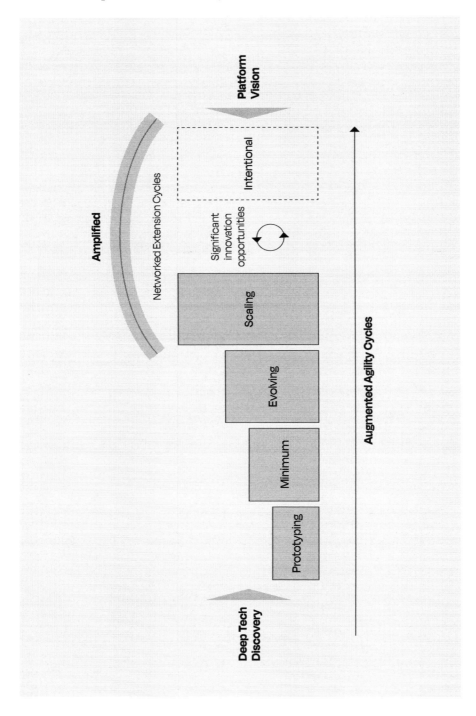

in exponential complexity and rigidness which Brian Foote and Joseph Yoder referred to as "big balls of mud anti-patterns".[102] Nowadays, when a platform's core, micro-services and service domains are not explicitly well-defined, the result is uncoordinated business events. In this situation, another complex anti-pattern emerges, often referred to by software developers as a 'Death Star anti-pattern'. These occur when the co-ordination between fragmented digital services reaches an exponential level of complexity which a platform's architecture cannot handle. A famous example occurred in the mid-2000s when Amazon's platform reached a level of complexity that was no longer manageable, forcing the platform to evolve new microservice management capabilities.[103]

This complexity can be managed through information hiding and clear event, service and data contracts. Information is managed in such a way that any party interested in an event has no structural coupling and dependency with the author of the event or with any other party that also has access to it. This means that any part of the platform can access the event and maintain the complexity while scaling its activities, allowing complex services to be continually replaced with more efficient ones without impacting on the performance of other services.

The backbone plays a central role in maintaining design coherence across every layer of the architecture and the boundaries of the services. It should not be thought of as a self-contained system; backbone links are present in every layer of the platform and provide a highly unified and efficient set of core capabilities to platform services. It is their ability to manage complexity which technically enables the elevation, scaling, and amplification of an organisation's value proposition.

SCALING WHOLE ENTERPRISES

Organisations can achieve scale and amplification through Deep Tech platforms by understanding their development lifecycle. Digital platforms are not simply defined, designed and implemented. They reach maturity after the platform architecture has passed through a number of distinct stages: prototyping, minimum, evolving, scaling, amplified and intentional (Figure 5.5).

We introduced the concept of intentional architecture in chapter four. Deep Tech platforms are designed by starting with an elevated value proposition. With this defined, it is then possible to develop a vision of the platform which is future-fit and which articulates the essence of the value proposition. An intentional architecture is never a fixed definition of the platform; it evolves continually as the platform matures. This facilitates a structured approach to platform design which consists of defining and planning architectural initiatives that support and enhance a platform's capabilities as it scales in the direction of the elevated vision.

Intentional architectures help people to understand the need to operate within certain boundaries, such as choice of technology platform, financial budget, design constraints or integration of future capabilities. When these constraint factors are identified and factored into the project, there is a greater chance that the initiative will be successful in delivering the elevated value proposition.

So while an intentional architecture defines a hypothetical end state that will never actually be built due to the evolutionary path of the platform, it provides the basis for the platform requirements which need to be defined before the first prototype is built. Following the prototyping stage, a minimum architecture is built with the first set of platform services. This minimum architecture allows designers to understand the emergent structures of the architecture better before progressing to the third stage, which is that of evolving architecture. This architecture is updated continuously through augmented agility iterative design cycles towards the vision of the intentional architecture.

Platforms develop through synchronised iterative cycles in order to maintain systemic integrity across the all levels of the platform—the backbone, the platform, its services and open interfaces. A platform architect therefore requires a high level of design consciousness in order to be able to understand a platform initiative as a dynamic living system. They have to be able to synchronise the future vision of the intentional architecture with the maturity of the current architecture and the functions and services added at each of the three main development stages: prototyping, minimum and evolution.

The platform architect must also ensure that the backbone has the requisite flexibility to be able to accompany the evolution of the platform architecture and the interoperability standards and protocols which allow every element of the platform to communicate with every other element. The backbone has to be open in order to be extensible but closed in relation to standardised interoperable protocols. Just as human backbones have a degree of solidity and rigidity but are flexible at the same time, so are digital backbones.

Having reached the evolving architecture stage, a platform can then be opened to a wider developer community who can add their own platform services, thereby moving the platform into a higher level of functioning, allowing it to achieve scale. This is the stage in which existing platform services can be amplified through new architectures. A platform can only be opened at this stage and not in the prior development stages because of the high likelihood of protocols changing or altering in some manner.

Two related software design laws can help us understand the progression towards platform maturity and develop platform vision:

The law of change: Every platform changes. A platform that does not change is no longer alive. Platforms therefore need to be thought of as a form of a living system.

The law of complexity: Every time a platform evolves, it becomes more complex. In becoming more complex, even more changes are introduced. The best way to lead with change and manage complex platforms and architectures is augmented agility, which we explain in the next chapter.

A living system can be characterised by the way in which information flows through it. Those people responsible for a platform initiative must ensure that the language they use to describe their designs is accessible and understandable to all stakeholders in the development. It is often the case that the language of platform architectures is technical and difficult to decipher, even by software developers and technology specialists.

The level of complexity of Deep Tech platforms means that leaders need to pay close attention to the co-ordination and synchronisation between the digital backbone, deep analytics, platform services, common growth layers and extension points. When developed by disparate teams or without proper integration, they can decouple from business development and enterprise design activities, creating a conflict between the business and technology operating systems. A platform's new business ecosystem logic therefore has to be aligned with established organisational structures by the senior executive team. When synchronisation is achieved across every layer, the organisation can strive forward towards its future-fit vision.

The synchronisation between a platform's services, the platform architecture and an organisation's business dynamics critically impacts on a platform's capacity to evolve and scale. The velocity of this evolution and the operational ability to manage the resulting complexity is enabled through deep collaboration between platform development teams, enterprise architects, senior leaders and departmental managers (marketing, sales, customer success, finance etc.). For this reason, the senior executive team needs to understand the nature of platform design conventions and how they relate to the way in which their organisation operates from both a business and technical perspective.

The increase in the complexity and distribution of advanced technologies has seen an expansion of perspectives in the operation of digital services. For example, DataOps focuses on automating data flows and analytics to and from service domains; MLOps focuses on user analytics and machine learning; DevSecOps focuses on the development, security and operations of digital services; and FinOps brings financial accountability to the variable spend model of cloud computing business models, enabling teams to make business trade-offs between speed, cost and quality.[104]

For these operational activities to function optimally, the relationship between platform scaling and its organisational enterprise architecture must be understood in relation to platform design conventions, architectural maturity, platform services and business capabilities. There is a direct relationship between platform design, team topology, leadership maturity and organisational alignment.[105] It is therefore the role of senior executive teams to help their organisations synchronise their platforms, teams and business processes. This synchronisation can only be achieved when leaders understand the way of thinking of technology architects, whose technological creativity comes from their mastery of design principles, patterns and practices in addition to their ability to build digital systems based on business processes and enterprise logic. For this reason, we will now explain how these patterns and practices relate to an organisation's operations.

A common term to describe the design and development of a platform is 'platform engineering'. Its metaphor suggests that a set of laws exist that can be mechanically followed to create a scalable architecture. In practice, it is platform design conventions rather than fixed laws that enable platforms to scale (Figure 5.6).

Our Deep Tech platform design methodology categorises these design conventions across three dimensions:

1. Patterns: Architectural development makes use of patterns rather than design laws. These patterns relate to enterprise design, team structures, innovation practices and team behaviour, together with technical design practices such as system analysis, design patterns, implementation style and automated testing.

2. Feedback: Architectural development requires the continual validation of the patterns through continuous feedback. Key activities include the definition of

FIGURE 5.6 Platform Design Conventions

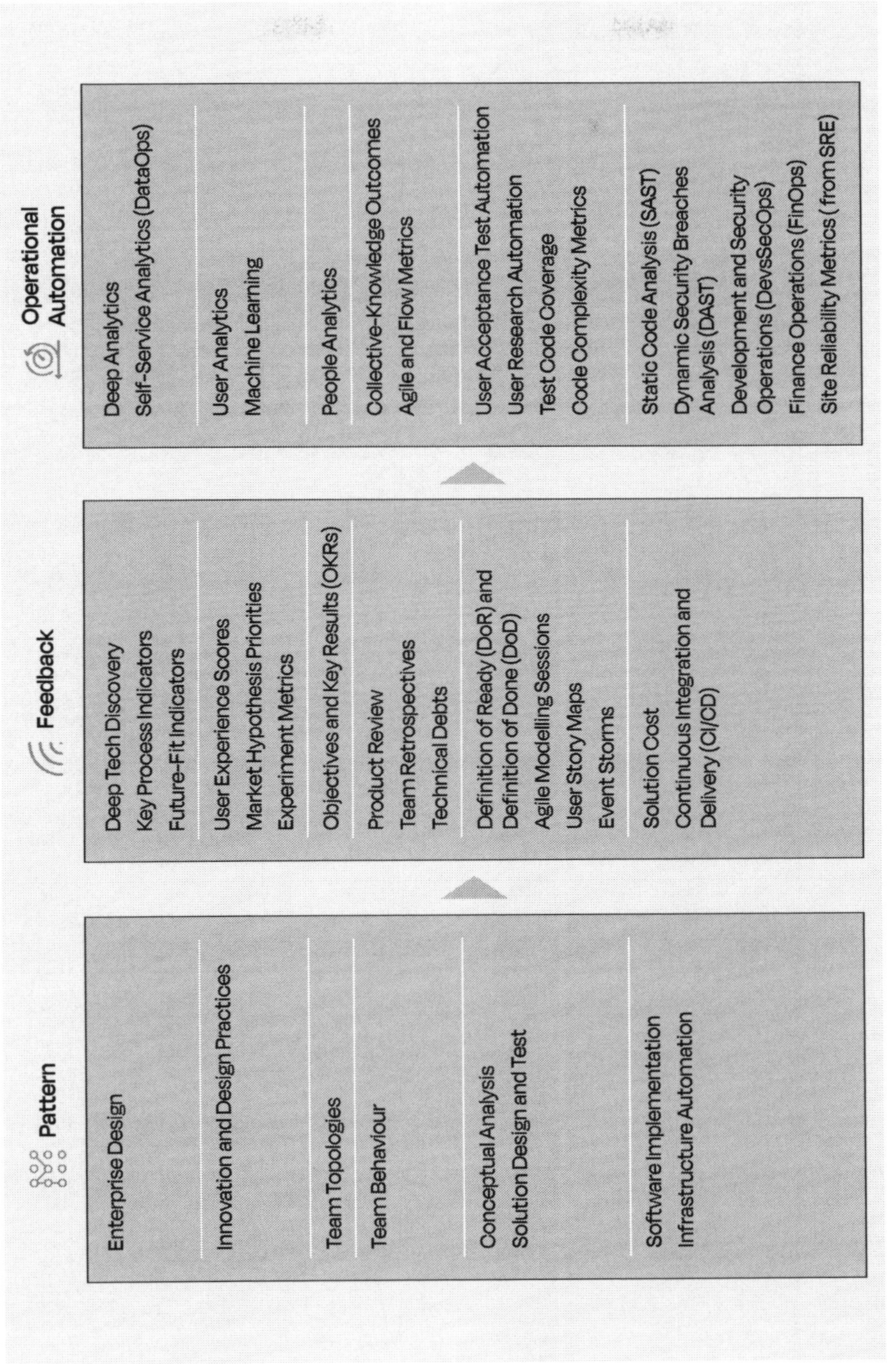

The figure is oriented as a rotated diagram with three main sections:

Pattern

- Enterprise Design
- Innovation and Design Practices
- Team Topologies
- Team Behaviour
- Conceptual Analysis
- Solution Design and Test
- Software Implementation
- Infrastructure Automation

Feedback

- Deep Tech Discovery
- Key Process Indicators
- Future-Fit Indicators
- User Experience Scores
- Market Hypothesis Priorities
- Experiment Metrics
- Objectives and Key Results (OKRs)
- Product Review
- Team Retrospectives
- Technical Debts
- Definition of Ready (DoR) and Definition of Done (DoD)
- Agile Modelling Sessions
- User Story Maps
- Event Storms
- Solution Cost
- Continuous Integration and Delivery (CI/CD)

Operational Automation

- Deep Analytics
- Self-Service Analytics (DataOps)
- User Analytics
- Machine Learning
- People Analytics
- Collective-Knowledge Outcomes
- Agile and Flow Metrics
- User Acceptance Test Automation
- User Research Automation
- Test Code Coverage
- Code Complexity Metrics
- Static Code Analysis (SAST)
- Dynamic Security Breaches Analysis (DAST)
- Development and Security Operations (DevSecOps)
- Finance Operations (FinOps)
- Site Reliability Metrics (from SRE)

FIGURE 5.7 Digital Platform Qualities

Digital business	Flexible Business Models	Amplified View of Markets	Dynamic Capabilities	Extensible Core	Unified Digital Operating Model
Service interfaces	Simple Interactions	Volume Functions	Ethical Exchange of Value	Intentional Network Effects	Terms of Use with Good Faith	Open Interfaces
Application design	Clear Domain Boundaries	Unified Language	Secure and Private Data	Unbiased AI	Updated Technology
Architectural principles	Elevated Value	Conceptual Integrity	Organising principles	Replicated Identity

key processes, future-fit indicators, experimental metrics, objectives and key results (OKRs), as well as acceptance and solution integration testing which require reliability, service quality and user experience metrics.

3. Operation Automation: Platforms need to be monitored and maintained regularly. Platform architectures must be continually observed using many different metrics to ensure that they will not break or fail.

Platform architectures which are not well-built suffer from over complexity and rigidity which limits their ability to scale. Rather than attempting to maximise the quality every single element in isolation, a good platform architect will search for the optimal level of growth and development of a platform, always seeking to optimise platform performance as a whole. Without this level of architectural optimisation, the scaling of the platform will be neither economic, secure nor integrated with an organisation's business operations. Platform architects therefore have a key leadership role in developing the quality of people's systemic vision and helping teams to understand how their particular work contributes to the overall strategy, implementation and functioning of the platform.

THE HUMAN DIMENSION

Deep Tech platforms can be differentiated from regular digital platforms by their collective qualities (Figure 5.7). This framework is based on our Deep Tech manifesto and demonstrates how the qualities of universal human values, the level of consciousness and understanding of soul in technology within the manifesto translate into future-fit digital economy solutions.

The Digital Business layer demonstrates that a fully empowered platform enables the flexibility and extension of services, sustains scale with high quality application design and has a solid foundation of architectural principles which define and characterise it as Deep Tech. The dynamic capabilities of platforms allow digital businesses to have more flexible business models through an amplified view of markets, due to their extensible core and unified digital operational model supported by backbones.

The Digital Business layer is made possible through Service Interfaces which consist of simple interactions. Volume Functions must be fair and communicated to users. Sensitive information or behavioural analytics should not be collected which do not directly enhance the service quality to users or which lock-in and make opting-out of the platform difficult.

Organisations which do this can face severe consequences. For example, when Android phones were first launched, users were only able to use the Chrome browser and could not install any others such as Firefox. As a result of these actions, the European Commission fined Google €4.34 billion for breaching EU antitrust rules.[106] Commenting on this action, Commissioner Margrethe Vestager, head of EU competition policy, said:

"Today, mobile internet makes up more than half of global internet traffic. It has changed the lives of millions of Europeans. Our case is about three types of restrictions that Google has imposed on Android device manufacturers and network operators to ensure that traffic on Android devices goes to the Google search engine. In this way, Google has used Android as a vehicle to cement the dominance of its search engine. These practices have denied rivals the chance to innovate and compete on their merits. They have denied European consumers the benefits of effective competition in the important mobile sphere. This is illegal under EU antitrust rules."[107]

The Exchange of Value relating to the relationship between users and Deep Tech platforms must therefore always be ethical and transparent, and not opaque. In 2018, Facebook's brand image was damaged globally by Cambridge Analytica which had improperly obtained personal data from 270,000 people who had downloaded a personality prediction application. This scandal caused Facebook to suffer the most significant loss of stock market value in a single day, with its shares closing down almost 19%, wiping USD 119 billion off the company value.[108]

Another example of an unethical exchange of value is when a platform intentionally adopts a closed set of standards and protocols, even when open alternatives already exist and are suitable for the service domain, thereby preventing other platforms from adopting them. Many dominant platform businesses have taken this approach in the past, forcing clients and consumers to use their solutions rather than those of their competitors.

To counter these less equitable forms of value exchange, in March 2021, Soundcloud, a music and audio platform, introduced fan-powered royalties on their platform as a more just and transparent way for emerging and independent artists to earn money. Fan-powered royalties are driven directly by an artist's fan base. Each listener's subscription or advertising revenue is distributed among the artists they listen to rather than via pooled plays, benefiting rising independent artists with loyal fans. To demonstrate the difference, Soundcloud's explanation of their new revenue model cited a real-case example of Vincent, an electronic artist who under the old plan was getting paid USD 120. The new model would allow him to receive USD 600, an increase of 403%.[109]

Michael Weissman, Chief Executive Officer, SoundCloud, explained the benefits of this elevated form of value exchange:

"Many in the industry have wanted this for years. We are excited to be the ones to bring this to market to better support independent artists. SoundCloud is uniquely positioned to offer this transformative new model due to the powerful connection between artists and fans that takes place on our platform. As the only direct-to-consumer music streaming platform and next-generation artist services company, the launch of fan-powered royalties represents a significant move in SoundCloud's strategic direction to elevate, grow and create new opportunities directly with independent artists."[110]

Platform development teams must also be fully conscious of systemic network effects. The reason is that without this level of design consciousness, a platform can potentially contribute and amplify inequality rather than reducing it. Poor accessibility, complex language use, unconscious social biases, cybersecurity and privacy concerns all have direct consequences on the value that a platform can deliver. Open interfaces also contribute to network effects, as they allow developer communities worldwide to adapt and specialise platform services that would not have been anticipated by the platform's original design team. Network effects therefore are responsible for the exponential impact of the platform.

An example of a conscious platform proposition comes from RideFair, a crowd-funded project to create an open-source driver co-op ridesharing platform. Their idea is to provide a non-profit open-source platform as an alternative to Uber, Lyft, Ola and Didi. The value exchange is articulated explicitly in RideFair's mission statement, which contains each dimension of the New 4Ps:

"Our mission is to help drivers earn a fair and equitable income by giving them the ability to claim ownership of the companies that they drive for. Having a co-op owned ridesharing business allows drivers to have a say in company decisions regarding policies, fare changes and the committee members steering the direction of the company. Moreover, drivers get to keep 95% of their hard-earned money as RideFair would only take a 5% cut from the fares to cover maintenance costs and development. This model empowers drivers to control their own destiny, and all proceeds remain within the local community, which is greatly beneficial for the long-term growth and sustainability of the local economy."[111]

The final quality relating to service interactions is the terms of use of the platform and good faith. By being present in every Deep Tech development, venture and initiative, good faith is a relational legal concept that articulates human values in practice. Legal jurisdictions worldwide treat good faith in different ways, some of which are more defined than others. For example, in English law, there is no general doctrine of good faith either in negotiating or performing a contract. However, English law does include the notion of 'relational contracts' where the parties are subject to duties of good faith as a matter of law. In these instances the parties are "prohibited from conduct which in the relevant context would be regarded as commercially unacceptable by reasonable and honest people".[112]

The Application Design layer refers to technical qualities. Service domain boundaries must be clearly defined in order to manage the complexity of the platform. The technical language which describes the platform must be unified to ensure that the platform serves technology specialists *and* is fully accessible by taking cultural differences into account. Language plays a critical role in amplifying access to the platform to both users and the broadest and diverse community of platform developers.

Data applications must be secure to guarantee users' privacy and always up to date with the latest technological developments. In addition, artificial intelligence algorithms should be as unbiased as possible. For example, these can come about due to the cognitive biases of the designers responsible for them or a lack of complete data resulting in non-representative samples being used. One example is Amazon's attempt in 2015 to automate its recruiting process by using AI to read and review candidate résumés. Within a short space of time Amazon realised that this process contained a systemic bias against women, leading it to stop using the algorithm in recruitment.[113]

The final layer of digital platform qualities is that of Architectural Principles. Our Deep Tech approach to platform design highlights the need to imagine how the value proposition can elevate our quality of life based on future-fit technologies which recognise our physical planetary resource limits and regenerative principles of living systems. For the elevated value proposition to be fully realised, it must be present conceptually in every aspect of the platform. It is at this point that a platform can be said to have conceptual integrity.

When a platform has this level of integrity, it becomes possible to replicate its identity; its DNA being present in every interaction and services provided. The wholeness of the technology is articulated through every part, with values, ethics, fairness and a unified language that expresses its singular essence and identity. Wholeness is a quality of a system that is encountered by people in their use and interaction with a platform. Platform architects and designers achieve this wholeness when the platform's qualities are manifested through three interconnected drivers (Figure 5.8).

FIGURE 5.8 Deep Tech Platform Drivers

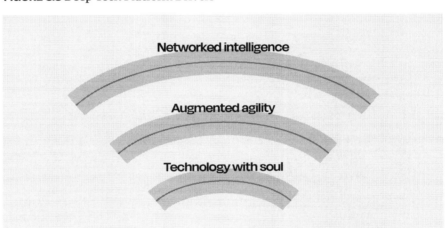

The way in which these three dimensions operate together systemically will be explored in detail in chapter six. We define them in the following way:

Technology with Soul: technology which facilitates a deep connection between the essence of an amplified organisation, its identity, culture and technological, social and environmental design challenges.

Augmented Agility: an accelerated pace of evolution that is galvanised by elevated relationships of collaboration and confidence, collective mastery and transformational leadership. The role of Augmented Agility is to scale Technology with Soul and facilitate Networked Intelligence.

Networked Intelligence: open collaboration ecosystems which contain layers of intelligence between organisations and which are made possible through standardised architectures with common protocols, ethical policies and privacy mechanisms.

Before an organisation can start to design and implement a Deep Tech platform that can deliver an elevated value proposition, the leadership team has to understand, identify and eliminate a number of interconnected digital platform inhibitors (Figure 5.9). We use these as a Deep Tech sensemaking framework for business leaders with whom we work when developing concurrent digital and cultural transformation initiatives.

No matter how great the desire, energy and resources for developing a platform, if the inhibitors are present, an organisation will lack the necessary conditions to enable the platform to elevate, scale and amplify to any meaningful degree. It is these inhibitors that prevent an organisation from achieving its greatest potential in the digital economy.

The first layer of inhibitors can be understood as those factors which lead to collective blurred vision within an organisation. This is where there is an ill-defined value proposition, the platform vision is poorly understood and not future-fit, and the overall strategy is not aligned with the organisation's Environmental, Social, and Governance (ESG) policy. An organisation's vision can also be blurred due to outdated incentives, policies and management systems which are no longer relevant for digital operating models.

In addition, an organisation's culture can be extremely resistant to change, especially where there are low levels of diversity and inclusion, resulting in the same ideas and mental models operating. Vision also suffers when there is a lack of qualified talent to design, implement and operate a new platform-based business model, preventing the organisation from understanding the link between strategy and execution.

It can be the case that the most senior levels of leadership lack the critical appreciation and understanding of the logic of platform architectures to make the most informed strategic decisions for their organisations. For this reason, when a strategy map is integrated into agile design processes, designers with strategic

FIGURE 5.9 Deep Tech Platform Inhibitors

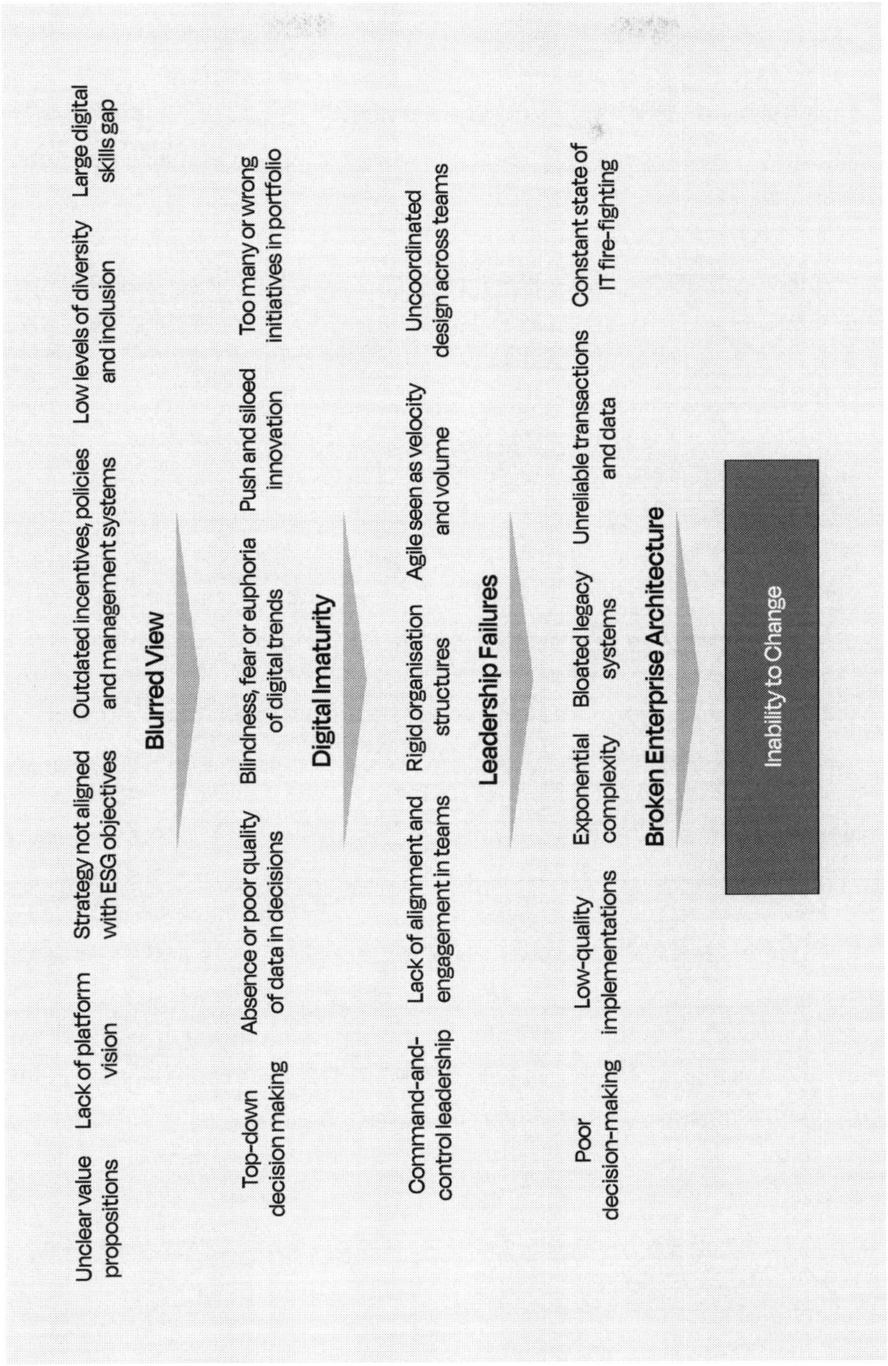

vision are better able to take on a more protagonistic role by owning responsibility for developing platform vision in the executive team. Organisations that collectively design well-constructed and systemic strategy maps are able to articulate the overall vision, the elevated valued proposition and mission-critical Deep Tech initiatives in a clear and meaningful manner and in a way in that is linked to the enterprise-level operations and strategy for managing, supporting and developing people.

The next category of inhibitors relates to the level of digital immaturity within an organisation. For example, some organisations are still over-reliant on top-down decision making, a form of leadership which is not suitable for agile initiatives and projects. The decision-making level in these contexts can often be deficient due to the lack of relevant data and analysis and driven by cognitive biases, limited mental models and unsuitable organisational cultures. Leaders need to be aware of levels of blindness, fear or over-reliance on digital trends in their businesses. The solution, as we will demonstrate in chapter six, is to integrate computational sensemaking with networked intelligence, a process which elevates an organisation's leadership and decision-making abilities to a higher level.

Digital immaturity relates to the level at which innovation is understood and embedded within an organisation. In some organisations innovation takes place in siloed departments with low levels of connection and communication with other areas. Organisations can also suffer from having too many or sub-optimal technology and innovation projects to manage. When an innovation is not well understood internally, it can be launched into markets prematurely and without the necessary fundamental qualities necessary for it to become a success.

A lack of digital maturity is a result of failures in leadership teams. Instead of agile, autonomous and highly strategic teams working in a networked fashion, the result is command-and-control forms of leadership which stifle innovation and technology initiatives. With too much controlling power focused at the top of an organisation, teams struggle to align and engage their people, resulting in poor communication and time and resources wasted correcting issues that would not have occurred with organisational structures more suited to agile ways of working.

Top-down driven organisations have the potential to suffer from over-rigid structures, meaning that they cannot respond to changing events rapidly. This is reflected in their conception of agile, seeing it as velocity and volume rather than flexibility and continual adaptation to changing requirements and business environments. The result is uncoordinated design teams, each producing and designing in their own way, without reference to either the systemic vision of the project or the strategy map. In these cases, platform structures are developed which do not integrate optimally with their digital backbones. The outcome is that the platform services do not create the expected customer experiences, with the logic of the enterprise architecture breaking down due to the level of complexity not being suitably managed and understood.

The final set of inhibitors are signals that should alert an organisation for the need to diagnose and rectify their specific digital platform inhibitors. This category of inhibitors can be challenging to manage because they result from an organisation's inability to change. When these inhibitors are present, platform development processes result in poor quality estimates of costs and ease or difficulty of execution, poorly implemented decision-making and unexpected exponential increases in platform complexity. Legacy systems exacerbate these challenges due to their inability to provide the features and qualities necessary for the advanced level of architecture envisioned. Transactions and data within these systems are unreliable, with IT departments being in a constant state of emergency, always firefighting rather than being proactive and strategic.

The overall result is a broken enterprise architecture which simply does not have the capability or capacity necessary to deliver amplified Deep Tech platforms. Taken collectively, the digital platform inhibitors can be used as a diagnostic to test the readiness of an organisation's culture for Deep Tech innovation and digital transformation. When identified and remedied by senior leaders in an organisation, the result is the design and implementation of Deep Tech initiatives that consider both digital and cultural transformation as two sides of the same coin. They are not factors that can or should be separated.

One of the most important insights for leadership teams to understand is that hard skills are often not the most difficult aspect of Deep Tech projects. It is the quality of the human dimension (often referred to disparagingly as 'soft skills') which impacts the most in a project's success. Failure to take the human dimension into account runs the risk of extremely expensive failure. When leaders understand that soft skills are in fact hard leadership skills requiring personal mastery, these inhibitors are taken seriously, diagnosed and rectified before attempting to launch wide-scale digital transformation initiatives.

Deep Tech leaders at every level of an organisation need to master value propositions, purpose, terminology and communication while at the same time demonstrating high levels of values, consciousness and systems thinking. They need competence in empathy skills to be able to understand not only the importance of the customer experience but also the employee experience and the developer experience. The way of being of an organisation is reflected in the quality of its relationships. So it is of vital importance for leaders to understand these inhibitors and how they impact on relationships, communication, design and strategic alignment. Ultimately, the role of Deep Tech leaders is to pay attention to the quality of relationships across both their organisations and business ecosystems. Without this level of systemic integrity, organisations and ecosystems will not be capable of designing and executing digital transformation with elevated value propositions that are future-fit.

The transformation to digital business models for the new economy always starts with an organisation developing an elevated platform vision. This is achieved in the discovery phase by aligning design practices through cross-organisational engagement. The most successful Deep Tech leaders understand that a digital platform and its architectural structures represent the co-ordination of the organisation's relationships because they are present in every system and every transaction. When the digital activities are well-coordinated inside the organisation, it becomes possible to operate platforms effectively and manage their expansion through their interfaces with the outside environment.

Organisations achieve scale through integrating their digital operating model with their digital platform architecture. This integration is achieved through computational ontologies which facilitate conversations across different enterprise domains. Figure 5.10 shows how this can be achieved.

An organisation's digital operating model consists of four interconnected layers. The first layer describes an organisation's technical foundations: cloud and on-premise digital infrastructures, technical reference architectures and advanced technology mechanisms which empower digital services. This technical layer facilitates the most appropriate way to integrate, standardise and select technology components and expand the computing power of digital platforms and solutions, enabling cost efficiencies and greater scale and flexibility of platforms.

The second layer refers to digital services. This is where automation, data analytics, artificial intelligence, digital innovation and security and privacy services are all located. While organisations generally do have expertise in the design of these differing services in relation to data and data structures, it is rare to find

FIGURE 5.10 Digital Operating Model

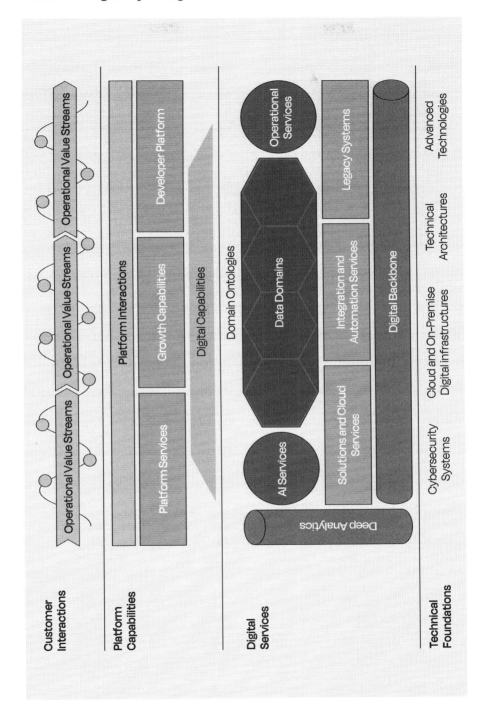

competence in the critical third dimension which is data domains (explained in chapter six).

The third layer describes an organisation's platform capabilities. This layer contains platform services, growth capabilities and developer services. The digital capabilities, offers and platform interactions are built using combinations of AI services and operational services provided by the digital services and technical foundations, hence they are located in a higher level layer of the model.

The final layer in the digital operating model is the customer journey. The platform vision, future-fit vision, strategic scenarios, transformation portfolio and roadmap collectively drive operational value stream enhancements and customer experience innovation. The digital operating model can only work as a whole when the transformation roadmaps and investment portfolio possess a business ontology (concepts, relational properties and data sets) which is shared across the three prior layers of platform capabilities, digital services and technical foundations. Without this business ontology, data domains cannot be structured, meaning that the full potential of the application services and technology is not attained.

Architecture is all about extending and enhancing the vitality of systems through a dynamic balance of forces and a continuously evolving process of learning and development. Our Deep Tech Discovery methodology enables organisations to scale by taking a more profound approach to platform design, resulting in the co-creation of simple yet powerful core sets of user interactions. Bold and urgently needed elevated value propositions require specialised and differentiated platform services that rely on a solid backbone and deep analytics intelligence, supported by growth capabilities. While the technical excellence of teams provides the integrity and fuel for platform development, it is the quality of the vision of the intentional architecture that ensures that the platform architecture is always aligned with the overall strategic purpose of the amplified organisation.

Executive Summary

→ Digital transformation is a journey of strategic business transformation. It is the shift in the way an organisation delivers value through the implementation of digital business models, digital operating models and digital platforms.

→ Organisations which do not possess platform vision do not differentiate between a platform's value proposition and the services that the platform offers. Platforms should always be built by first defining this value proposition before its services. It is the services that make possible and amplify the value proposition and not the other way around.

→ The purpose of a platform is to provide value through the implementation of digital business models, digital operating models and digital platforms.

→ The backbone is the unified foundation of core processes, data, applications and technologies. It is the nucleus of the platform.

→ Deep analytics must be operated within an organisation's frameworks for data privacy and ethics governance. These define the policies and verification mechanisms to support the development of analytical and deep learning models in a manner that is as unbiased and as fair as possible.

→ Deep Tech platform inhibitors provide a diagnostic framework for leadership teams to understand the level of digital platform maturity within their organisations. The most important inhibitors to digital innovation are not technical or financial, but are instead related to the cultural, cognitive, social and digital maturity of an organisation.

→ The purpose of the digital platform is to orchestrate the relationships within the organisation's digital ecosystem. A strategy of digital platforms has to be designed by Deep Tech leaders to ensure organisation-wide alignment. This strategy requires a deep understanding of the market space, the customer value proposition, purpose, digital platform architecture, technology infrastructures, digital services, platform capabilities and the digital operating model.

6

CHAPTER SIX

Purpose-Centred Design

TECHNOLOGY WITH SOUL

In chapter three we discussed living systems to show that the way in which we understand systems impacts on how we make sense of the world. There are many different ways to think about and understand systems, and as we saw, this includes taking into account the four different ways of knowing the world: thinking, feeling, sensing and intuition. In chapter five we then explained the importance of systems thinking in relation to platform vision and understanding complex platform architectures.

Organisations build their technical architectures in qualitatively different ways, due for example, to the context of technology or difference in technical skills in design teams. So to implement a digital transformation strategy we therefore need to know how to analyse the context of the organisation and its architectures. The way we can do this is to use the same processes by which we understand the organising principles of living systems.

With platform-based business models becoming so predominant in the digital economy, many organisations are now struggling with issues of complexity, unmanageably high volumes of data, a lack of data integrity and rigid legacy systems.

In the digital economy, the winners will be those organisations with leaders who are able to learn to see the patterns and connections of complex relationships. This can be achieved by deep contemplation of different aspects of living system.

Our approach to Deep Tech is designed to help lift organisations out from a singular technological perspective to a more planetary one. The way we do this is to take inspiration from the design practices of biomimetics (also known as bio-mimicry). Rather than attempt to transfer a concept or mechanism from living to digital systems through simple and direct replicas of the biological prototype, we look to take a more analogical perspective, starting by imagining technological systems as being situated inside of biological ones.

Austrian biologist Ludwig von Bertalanffy was one the originators of general systems theory, first developed in the 1940s, who had sought to find a new approach to understanding living systems.[114] While this way of understanding systems is predominantly functional, general systems theory is useful for understanding categories of system and their scale, and determining boundaries between open and closed systems and the self-organised relationships between matter, energy and information. For example, the Milky Way contains between 100 and 400 billion stars. The human brain contains approximately 86 billion neurones. While these are of a similar scale, the organising principles and the relationships between the parts in the systems are radically different.

When we contemplate living systems, their scale and qualities are astounding. For example:

- There are 8.7 million living species on Earth;
- The population of the world's top 10 known animals (including humans) is 14 billion;
- There are 30 billion cells in the human body;
- There are 37 billion viruses in the human body;
- There are 3.04 trillion trees on the planet.[115]

Our contemporary technological systems are extremely powerful and function at an incredible scale. For example, in 2017, 20 trillion transistors per second were produced globally (the basic unit of digital equipment).[116] In August 2020, just three years later, Cerebras announced the Cerebras CS-1—"the world's most powerful AI computer system". This 8.5 inch-square chip, powered by 1.2 trillion transistors, is so fast and powerful it can predict future actions "faster than the laws of physics produce the same result".[117] The reason for producing this AI technology is to improve on deep learning training models by allowing researchers to "experiment with strange tensor shapes, irregular network structures, very sparse networks and much more, without the performance penalties levied by existing devices".[118] This allows researchers to be vastly more productive by "reducing the time it takes to train models from months to minutes and from weeks to seconds".[119]

In 2021, Cerebras managed to more than double the number of transistors per chip by launching the Wafer Scale Engine 2 (WSE-2) with 2,600 trillion transistors, accelerating artificial intelligence and machine learning workloads even further.[120] The move into quantum computing suggests that computer scientists are not that far away from developing a new generation of computer which can solve real-world problems that traditional computers simply cannot handle. While Google had previously held the world record for the world's fastest quantum computer, in July 2021, Jian-Wei Pan and a team of colleagues from the University of Science and Technology of China in Hefei and his colleagues reported that their programmable quantum computer named Zuchongzhi had solved a problem in just over an hour that would have taken the world's most powerful supercomputer eight years to solve.[121]

The internet traffic per second in July 2021 was measured at 121,858 gigabytes.[122] It is important though not only to consider the computational power of technology. It is also important to consider the social dimension of technological systems is the. For example, the technology most responsible for the adoption and exponential usage of the internet is video. To understand the speed of this growth, *Baby Cha Cha Cha*, the first internet video meme of a baby dancing rendered in 3D, was designed and released in 1996. Twenty years later, Pinkfong, a South Korean education company, turned the campfire song *Baby Shark* into a video that spread virally through social media, online video and radio. By November 2020, it had become the most-viewed video on YouTube of all time, with over 8.3 billion views.[123]

Donella Meadows, one of the world's most influential systems thinkers, defined systems in the following manner:

"So what is a system? A system is a set of things—people, cells, molecules or whatever—interconnected in such a way that they produce their own pattern of behaviour over time. The system may be buffeted, constricted, triggered, or driven by outside forces. But the system's response to these forces is characteristic of itself, and that response is seldom simple in the real world."[124]

Figure 6.1 shows the way in which thinking about the qualities of living systems can help us better understand the relationships between technological, human and ecological systems, and therefore allow us to better design future-fit Deep Tech solutions with more meaningful purposes.

FIGURE 6.1 Interconnections Between Living Systems

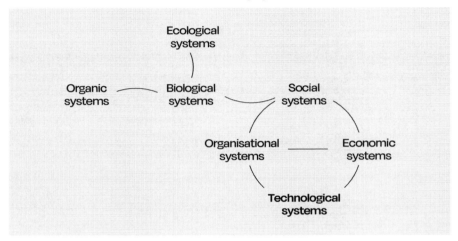

As humans, we are living first and foremost inside of an ecological system which consists of organic systems, biological systems and social systems. These organic systems—living and non-living—allow the conditions for biological systems to exist, which have, in turn, given rise to sociological systems. These can be divided into organisational and economic systems, such as businesses, institutions, governmental organisations, states and countries.

Our technological systems can be seen as a result of the need to increase power within our organisational and economic systems. So here we can see that these three systems—organisational, economic and technological—are all fundamentally sociological systems, their principle components being social relationships. We have framed these systems in relation to ecological systems to emphasise the need to understand them as a whole, in the context of our planet, and not as somehow separate with more limited interactions. The value of any ecological system is in its networked structure and in its long-term maintenance as a whole, and not in the maintenance of a limited subset of parts. With this framing, technological systems are not subordinate to ecological systems, but are oriented by social systems which in turn are oriented by organic and biological systems.

We define 'technology with soul' as being those technological systems designed with purpose where the direction is always towards living systems. It is developed and designed intentionally in service to life, contributing to the maintenance, enhancement and regeneration of our social and ecological systems. When we do not have this conscious intention about technology, our innovations and design initiatives remain technology-oriented (Figure 6.2).

FIGURE 6.2 Technology-Oriented Development

This perspective starts with the imperative to produce a profit, driven by understanding and then manipulating consumer behaviour. Market opportunities are identified and solutions developed based on mechanistic design and management practices. These are ones in which there is no sense of a living and embedded connection between the technology-oriented innovation and the wider systemic impacts on our social and ecological systems.

Our Deep Tech purpose-centred approach to design, guided by the New 4Ps, takes the opposite approach. The development of Deep Tech solutions is oriented by the deep challenges we are now facing globally. These challenges require new design methods which are based on collaborative practices and informed by the principles of diversity, inclusion and lived experience. The result of these practices is life-oriented design and innovation, the aim of which is to contribute to the evolution of our social and environmental ecosystems.

Purpose-centred design therefore has the aim of facilitating a shift in the direction of our thinking from technology as the focus of development to a profound understanding of our global challenges; positing these as the drivers for techno-logical innovation. Technology is developed in service to life and innovation be-comes regenerative and flourishing due to the quality of its relationships within the wider global organic, biological and social systems.

FIGURE 6.3 Purpose-Centred Design

An appreciation of the qualities found in living systems, including our own bod-ies, can significantly elevate our design practices. Within the twelve major sys-tems of the human body we find many interesting design principles to inspire our technological developments and innovations (Figure 6.4). So, for example, while growth is incremental, the human body does not grow beyond certain boundary conditions; not doing so would result in damage and death. The metabolic system maintains a critical degree of synchronisation between sub-systems while other critical elements such as the heart and brain are heavily protected. In order to maintain health, many indicators are brought together which orientate action, such as the signal for hunger.

In the human body, we see an integrated, continual and real-time intelligent mea-surement system which is characterised by the systemic level of interconnections between each part. The nervous system, for example, consists of the brain, spinal cord and nerves. Nerves are cylindrical bundles of fibres that start in the brain and central spinal cord and branch out to different parts of the body.[125] Responses are triggered by the level of each alarm such as glucose, temperature and nutrition. They are also integrated, meaning that they do not just send signals from source to the cerebrum; they are configured into a network structure, dialoguing between each other.

FIGURE 6.4 Purpose-Centred Design Principles (i)

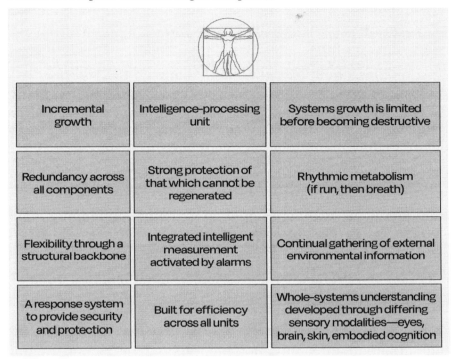

Incremental growth	Intelligence-processing unit	Systems growth is limited before becoming destructive
Redundancy across all components	Strong protection of that which cannot be regenerated	Rhythmic metabolism (if run, then breath)
Flexibility through a structural backbone	Integrated intelligent measurement activated by alarms	Continual gathering of external environmental information
A response system to provide security and protection	Built for efficiency across all units	Whole-systems understanding developed through differing sensory modalities—eyes, brain, skin, embodied cognition

The security of the human body does not arise through the certainty that no external damaging entities will invade. The body maintains its security by having appropriate immunological responses when harmful elements do inevitably enter. Likewise, organisations need to learn how to develop their digital systems to behave with the appropriate responses to risks, crises and electronic invasions. They also need to develop a sense of wholeness, one of the totality of the system rather than a hierarchical, mechanistic or departmentalised conception. This sense of wholeness comes from a way of thinking which integrates differing senses, lenses and feelings.

At times, an organisation only operates through a limited subset of lenses, the principle ones being financial and numerical. In these cases, the potential which comes through the full contributions of everyone in the organisation becomes lost through a lack of inclusion, diversity, emotional intelligence, creativity, sensemaking and decision-making. Organisations become able to amplify when they collect a wider range of both qualitative and quantitative data and information, process these through many differing lenses, and operate not just through a limited form of cognition, but from an expanded level of consciousness, allowing them to fully realise their authentic purpose.

A second source of living-systems inspiration comes from the qualities of integrity and replicability in DNA (Figure 6.5). The key behaviours of replication, diversification and spreading are critical for a system to have a long life. From a purpose-centred design perspective organisations must therefore be able, for example, to combine and integrate products with new ideas for diversification into new markets. If this is not happening, an organisation runs the risk of failing to survive in the longer term.

FIGURE 6.5 Purpose-Centred Design Principles (ii)

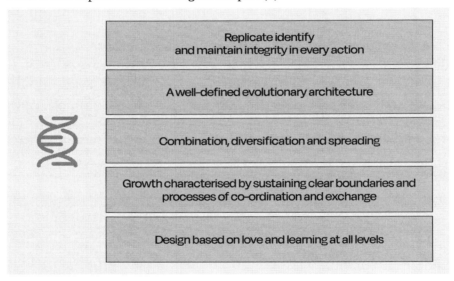

When we examine cells we can see that they have a well-defined architecture and evolutionary roles, i.e., there are specific cells for lungs, kidneys, heart, etc. All of these cells grow guided by the same architecture while having their separate responsibilities. This growth is defined by clear boundaries, co-ordinated action and the exchange of materials and energy. When an organisation is able to grow and develop through following these principles, every single part of the organisation evolves as a coherent living whole.

Learning how to see systems in new ways can enhance our existing design practices by helping unearth new systemic patterns and hidden qualities which may previously have remained undiscovered. When we immerse ourselves in a study of nature, encountering the quality of livingness in its systems, the opportunities to learn and be inspired are endless. The result is both a functional and structural vision of systems which respect the principles of living systems. When an organisation fully articulates the essence of technology with soul, technological solutions are able to reach a more transcendental level of design and universal human values. The physicist David Bohm articulated this notion by observing that:

"The field of the finite is all that we can see, hear, touch, remember, and describe. This field is basically that which is manifest, or tangible. The essential quality of the infinite, by contrast, is its subtlety, its intangibility. This quality is conveyed in the word 'spirit', whose root meaning is 'wind or breath.' This suggests an invisible but pervasive energy, to which the manifest world of the finite responds. This energy, or spirit, infuses all living things, and without it any organism must fall apart into its constituent elements. That which is truly alive in living systems is this energy of spirit, and this is never born and never dies."[126]

What Bohm is exploring is the notion of an animating spirit, without which an entity reduces to its constituent parts. Technology with soul is a concept which directs us towards a consideration of the correct place and direction of technology, seeking inspiration from that which animates us. Without this transcendental level of design, we will only be designing constituent parts and not a living organism.

Frankenstein's monster personifies this concept of lifeless design. His creation utilised the most advanced technology known to humanity, yet what was constructed was a vision of horror—a monster which was neither fully robot nor fully human and which was functionally and aesthetically abominable. The story creates a shock in us due to the way in which the parts are all in their correct place, and yet the whole fails to achieve its elevated purpose. It teaches us the degree to which we are creating technological systems which we neither not want nor need. Some parts may be of the highest quality, but the whole remains compromised.

Wholeness in a system is not simply defined by the relationships between the parts. We encounter wholeness in our experience of the system, and this is exactly why we need to learn how to develop many different techniques for understanding systems, such as the dynamic way of seeing and encountering phenomena such as colour, rather than being stuck in just an engineering lens of understanding light as an abstract and mathematical construct. When the quality of livingness is missed in our design practices, the outcomes are impoverished approximations to that which was intended.

Leaders can elevate the thinking of their organisations by helping people to appreciate the situational values of technology:

- Identity
- Self-expression
- Trust
- Diversity
- Inclusion
- Freedom of choice
- Opportunity for change
- Democracy
- Transparency

These situational values articulate the ways in which technology is able to be associated with the five universal human values of peace, truth, love, righteousness and non-violence. In this way, it becomes possible to put a universal value such as love into practice by developing systems which are based on trust and confidence. So while people express universal human values, the technology we build articulates their related situational values.

We can see human values being expressed in the four laws of sustainability which Donella Meadows proposed to help guide the development of purpose-centred designs:

1. Every renewable resource must be used at or below the rate at which it can regenerate itself;
2. Every non-renewable resource must be used at or below the rate at which a renewable substitute can be developed;
3. Every pollution stream must be emitted at or below the rate at which it can be absorbed or made harmless;
4. To be socially sustainable, capital stocks and resource flows must be equitably distributed and sufficient to give a good life to everyone.[127]

We achieve purpose-centred design when we bring together the values of technology and these laws of sustainability, elevating functional technology to technology with soul. It is within technology with soul we find the heart of Deep Tech. Figure 6.6 defines the meaning of technology with soul in relation to specific technologies.

The Soul of Technologies represents a framing of Deep Tech that allows us to develop an understanding of the purpose and elevated value proposition of advanced technology. So, for example, the internet is the collective cerebrum of the planet. Big Data represents our global sensing systems and automation and robotics can be thought of as limbs which free us from tedious, inane and repetitive tasks. The reason for developing this framing is that these technologies are the building blocks for the revolution which is taking us into the digital economy based on platform-based business models and value propositions. Purpose-centred technology promotes and gives rise to justice and health in democratic societies in which everyone is able to participate fully and have a constructive role to play.

AUGMENTED AGILITY

In chapter two we explored universal human values in relation to developing an authentic purpose in organisations. In this chapter we have shown how these values also relate to Deep Tech by taking a purpose-centred approach to its design and implementation. A third area of which universal human values are intrinsically a part is that of agile design methodologies. The reason is that when universal human values are present we require fewer rules and less bureaucracy. The quality of our relationships is also significantly higher, meaning that the way we collaborate becomes more meaningful, productive and less wasteful due to less jealousy, anger, criticism of others and attachment to our own ideas.

Our collaborations become more agile when we are able to nurture and facilitate authentic networks, rather than counterfeit *knotworks*, a term we created to characterise collaborative networks where high levels of ego are present.[128] When thinking about an organisational culture, when the universal human values of peace, truth, love, righteousness and non-violence are present and fully lived by each and every member, communities are able to develop flourishing and thriving cultures which allow each member to reach their highest potential and organisations to reach what we term 'higher ground'.

An organisation is operating from higher ground when it has the ability to develop elevated value propositions and meet the social, ecological and

FIGURE 6.6 The Soul of Technologies

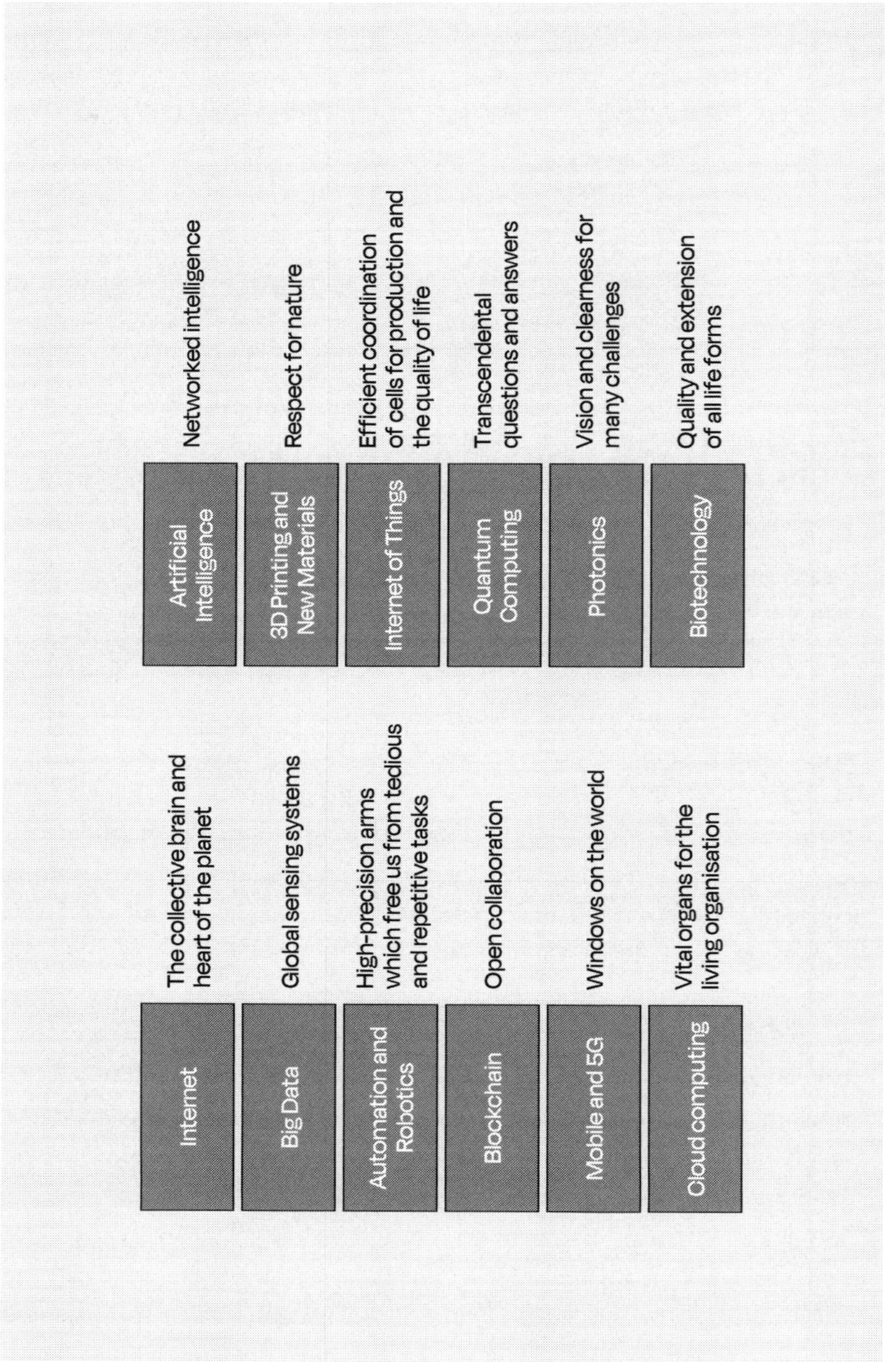

Internet	The collective brain and heart of the planet
Big Data	Global sensing systems
Automation and Robotics	High-precision arms which free us from tedious and repetitive tasks
Blockchain	Open collaboration
Mobile and 5G	Windows on the world
Cloud computing	Vital organs for the living organisation
Artificial Intelligence	Networked intelligence
3D Printing and New Materials	Respect for nature
Internet of Things	Efficient coordination of cells for production and the quality of life
Quantum Computing	Transcendental questions and answers
Photonics	Vision and clearness for many challenges
Biotechnology	Quality and extension of all life forms

technological vision of Deep Tech. Its social networks become psychologically, socially and biologically healthy, authentic and self-sustaining. In doing so, an organisation is able to evolve from the implementation of agile methodologies to the implementation of augmented agility, the foundation of which is an expanded and elevated form of consciousness.

It is not always the case that an organisation which implements agile methodologies automatically achieves agility. Traditionally, the focus of organisations adopting agile has been on the mechanics of methodologies such as SAFe®, a framework for scaling agile at the enterprise level. This framework was developed to drive faster time-to-market, achieve increases in productivity and quality and improve employee engagement.[129] If SAFe is implemented in a linear manner with a focus on the tools and rituals and not with an underlying understanding of the essence of agility, many expensive and time-consuming mistakes are likely to be made.

One of the reasons for this lack of understanding is that the original agile manifesto, articulated in four key values, refers to neither an organisation's strategy nor its value proposition:

i.   Individuals and interactions over processes and tools
ii. Working software over comprehensive documentation
iii. Customer collaboration over contract negotiation
iv. Responding to change over following a plan[130]

When we look to the twelve principles of agile, their focus is on software development rather than taking a systemic enterprise-wide perspective which incorporates strategy and value proposition definition. The principles which come closest to strategy are the first which states that, "Our highest priority is to satisfy the customer through early and continuous delivery of valuable software" and the fourth that, "Business people and developers must work together daily throughout the project".[131] We have observed many times first-hand that when high-profile agile development projects do not include strategic considerations, the result is a lack of strategy awareness and alignment in agile squads and teams.

Because of the paucity of strategy and value proposition alignment within the agile manifesto, which has not been updated since its conception in 2001, 1STi and Holonomics have worked together to develop a number of agility practices to improve the development and delivery of complex and challenging Deep Tech initiatives. Our Augmented Agility principles describe the characteristics which must be present for an organisation to achieve enterprise-wide agility:

i.   A clear strategic understanding of the challenges
ii.   Connection with the challenge
iii.   Confidence and collaboration
iv.   Elevated relationships
v.   Personal mastery
vi.   Universal human values

All of these principles can be seen in the augmented agility project in which 1STi were invited to participate with Hospital Sírio-Libanês in January of 2021, in the middle of the Covid-19 pandemic in Brazil. In the space of a single week, 1STi came together with an agile team from the hospital to design, test and launch an application to enable one thousand front-line workers to schedule and have their Covid vaccines. There were many major challenges in this project such as validating staff in relation to their identity, eligibility, their having potential symptoms, co-ordination of vaccination slots and vaccine manufacturer, etc., all within the context of a medical pandemic which was already putting unprecedented demands on the organisation.

On the night of Thursday the 14th of January, Igor received a call from the hospital notifying him that the vaccines would be approved in Brazil that following week. From this moment on, 1STi jumped into action to understand how a scheduling application could be developed. The team consisted of Igor as the overall application architect and communication leader, Eric Couto as project manager, Tiago Braga Machado as chief engineer, Ygor Fonseca as the front end designer, Arthur Couto as the back end designer, Ulli Maia as the interface designer, Maria Luciano as the tester and Igor Postiga as the consultant designer. Hospital Sírio-Libanês contributed with a product leader, an application manager and a data specialist.

Diego Aristides, Enterprise Agility Advisor and Senior IT Manager, explained to us the experience of working with augmented agility from the perspective of the hospital:

"This was a project where our clients were internal. Doctors, infectious disease specialists, administrators and technologists all worked together in incredible harmony, allowing us to implement the first version of the application, improve the vaccination process and evolve the products in just four days. Augmented agility allowed us to walk together, making and then correcting mistakes rapidly. In fact it felt that the team was so united that we no longer distinguished between people's different areas. This allowed us to really deliver our mission—a mission of delivering hope."

Many people came together quickly to develop an organisation-wide perspective on what would need to happen for the application to be designed and launched. With no margin for error, the application was designed across the weekend and validated with medical staff on the Monday and Tuesday, data was loaded and operational scripts implemented on the Wednesday, and the application launched on the Thursday, an incredible achievement. In every single aspect of this project, all of the principles of augmented agility were present, starting with a clear understanding of the challenge.

Ailton Brandão, Chief Information Officer at Hospital Sírio-Libanês spoke to us about how the augmented agility process had contributed to the success of the project:

"I believe it was the high engagement and high degree of contribution from everyone involved. Everyone had been waiting a long time for their vaccination. An unorganised vaccination procedure could have created chaos for us, running the potential risk of contamination for our collaborators. So augmented agility allowed each participant to feel part of the whole and being able to contribute their expertise and talent to their fullest potential. The satisfaction of seeing the application being born and then successfully working right from the start generated a lot of energy. It's amazing how a motivated group with the right organisation can deliver so much in such a short time. Augmented agility allows people to work without attachment and respects everyone's contribution."

Everyone in an augmented agility project needs to fully understand the strategic objectives. This is to allow them to fully engage with the challenge, always seeking to understand the critical success factors and maintaining a focus on working through the challenges, such as guaranteeing security and data protection in the application. Problems which are identified can only be solved through a high level of collaboration and confidence in each member of the team. When elevated levels of trust, transparency and empathy are present in an augmented agility project, the focus shifts from the chosen methodology to the dynamism and energy which allows for rapid adaption and problem solving. When an issue was identified with the formatting of data in one of the databases, for example, all team members worked together to ensure that no one was blamed, allowing all of the energy to be directed towards finding a solution. This level of team work can only ever be achieved through trust and not on apportioning blame or refusing to take ownership of a situation.

It was interesting to understand augmented agility from the perspective of one of the senior medical team who contributed to the project, Dr. Felipe Duarte Silva, Manager of Inpatients and Medical Practices:

"Working in a crisis scenario is challenging for any professional. Colleagues who dedicate their best efforts and those in management who are called upon to use the best of their abilities in an agile and creative way are able to design solutions that can resolve conflicts and also optimise work streams, thereby generating value. The Covid-19 pandemic has demanded a huge amount from us. However, imbued with a single purpose, it has also seen our unity grow and created the opportunity to collaborate more.

"The development of the application to organise and manage the vaccine campaign in Hospital Sírio-Libanês was definitely one of the great milestones of this work. In addition to promoting interaction and transparency for users, it brought efficiency in the way we managed the organisation of the process. It helped to avoid wasting resources and allowed us to adhere extremely closely to the formal guidelines of the various regulatory bodies regarding the municipal immunisation policy. We are better when we work together."

Augmented agility arises as a result of both high-functioning transformational leadership and technical mastery in order to be able to rapidly assess risks and determine the optimal direction at every decision point. Many organisations suffer due to a cultural imperative to find and blame culprits resulting in a loss of time and a huge expenditure of emotional energy. But when universal human values are applied and lived, people are able to express empathy, collaborate more intelligently and ensure that they respect the limits of each members' technical mastery and learning requirements. When they are present, higher levels of trust and communication mean that more decentralised reporting, decision making and operational structures become possible. This is not because people have learned a new agile methodology; it is because they have absorbed augmented agility as a way of being. As Ulli Maia explains:

> "One of the critical success factors in this project was the close contact that 1STi had with the team members at Hospital Sírio-Libanês. Due to the confidence and trust, 1STi were given a high level of autonomy, allowing us to adapt to each challenge and changing circumstance that arose."

Ulli has identified the following 'facilitators' which must be present in an augmented agility project for it to be successful. These are a checklist that can be discussed in the formative stages of a project to help align team members around purpose, expectations and values:

1. Fully-integrated and decentralised client and consultancy teams
2. Constant communication
3. Aligned expectations and priorities
4. Clearly defined application flows
5. Clearly defined business rules
6. Autonomous decision making
7. Complete understanding of the client culture and operations
8. Animated prototype screens

Ulli created this facilitator checklist having observed in many projects that designers are often not fully included in agile project management activities, especially at the strategic level. As he explains:

> "We designers are also part of agile projects and are responsible for development teams. For this reason, we also need to be actively inside of agile methodologies. As a designer I really focused on understanding the needs of Hospital Sírio-Libanês, and this was possible due to having direct contact with the client, something that not all designers are allowed. This was a critical factor which allowed our team to understand the user flows of the application in just one day, for example".

Augmented agility focuses on the human dimension of agility projects, enabling organisations to reach higher ground. As we have continually emphasised, it no longer makes sense to differentiate and separate digital transformation from cultural transformation initiatives. The vision of Deep Tech, as articulated in our manifesto, is one of augmented intelligence through the combination of artificial intelligence and conscious human endeavour. For this to happen, organisations need to learn how to transcend the challenges they have with the way in which they collect and analyse data through computational sensemaking and networked intelligence, the subject of the following section.

COMPUTATIONAL SENSEMAKING AND NETWORKED INTELLIGENCE

In chapter two we discussed the manner in which universal human values describe our essence as human beings. But we human beings are also human doings, and one of the most fundamental activities that we do, either consciously or unconsciously, is continually attempt to make sense of our world. Despite this desire, advances in the fields of psychology and neurobiology have still not provided an exact scientific and universally agreed understanding of how we do so.

Philosophy has contributed to our understanding of how we make sense of the world through the development of two branches. Ontology is a branch of metaphysics which explores questions of being and existence. Epistemology studies the question of the nature, origin and limits of human knowledge. The challenge for philosophy, therefore, is to endeavour to discover essential truths within the human act of interpretation, given that people experience worlds which are meaningful to them.

To help leaders develop an appreciation of the impact of interpretation, mental models and culture in their organisations, and to develop empathy towards the lived experience of both their external customers and their internal collaborators, Maria and Simon created the *Ladder of Seeing*, a schematic which is used to facilitate discussions around how we make sense of the world.[132] Each step represents a progressively more conscious appreciation of the impact that mental models have on our ways of seeing, and the stance that people take when asking questions and making assumptions about those questions and hypotheses they are testing. To see well is an act of humility. When leaders have the ability to step out of ego and engage in genuine dialogue to explore questions, scenarios and positions, they are able to help their organisation as a whole develop an amplified and more systemic vision which values diversity and inclusion and which does not collapse into to groupthink.

FIGURE 6.7 The Ladder of Seeing

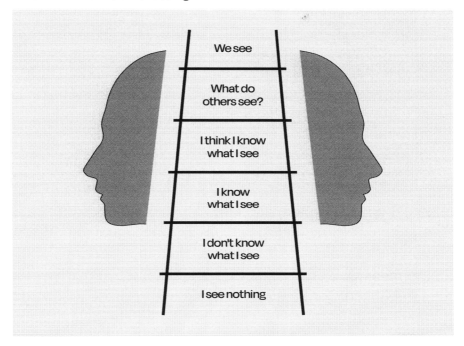

We see

What do others see?

I think I know what I see

I know what I see

I don't know what I see

I see nothing

The Ladder of Seeing was created as a tool to help leaders understand the process by which phenomena in the world appear to us as meaningful and to help to clarify to them potential limitations in their own ways of knowing reality. They are encouraged to explore their leadership styles, cognitive biases and co-creation processes through an empathic understanding of the world views, mental models and lived experience of other people who they may have otherwise ignored or failed to consult. It has been used by a number of teams in different organisational contexts as a diagnostic framework to help understand how and where dialogue and communication needs to be improved and utilised to help align people and strategic initiatives.

In the last two decades, organisations have faced the massive challenge of collecting, processing and storing big data; a term used to describe high volume, high velocity and highly variable data. We can extend the scope of the Ladder of Seeing from questions of leadership, design and innovation into the field of computational cognition. This allows us to explore the way in which humans, together with artificial intelligence, can make sense of the world collectively. In order to achieve this, we need to make the shift from big data to computational sensemaking. The catalyst for this shift is computational ontologies.

When an organisation understands computational ontologies, it has the ability to become amplified through its mastery of data, information and knowledge. Just as digital backbones provide the essential foundations for digital architectures, computational ontologies provide the essential foundations for enterprise architectures and digital operating models. They enable organisations to standardise and align complex digital architectures with enterprises goals, objectives and business functions.

Ontology in philosophy is an interpretative activity that seeks to provide insights into how people make sense of the world. Computational ontologies are designed to help researchers make sense of data which has been collected, categorised and stored. Joice Machado, 1STi's data scientist, explains what they are and how specialists in computational ontologies use them:

> "We use ontologies to create a way for information to be shared between people, data bases and applications. Ontology can be understood as the formal specification of a fixed domain. So once the domain has been defined, ontologists work within the context of both that domain and the organisation, defining relationships, properties and axioms in order to transform the information held within data bases and data lakes into knowledge. So ontologies are associated with machine learning models and algorithms, and help us to visualise the connections and relationships between disparate data."

Because an ontology consists of formal axioms and mathematically defined properties, it then becomes possible to interrogate the ontology using formal reasoning to allow a researcher to discover patterns and inferences in the data which is normally not possible due to the scale and volume of the data available. An example is ClinicalTrials.gov, a US web-based resource that provides patients, health care professionals and researchers with open access to information on publicly and privately supported clinical studies on a wide range of diseases and conditions. The web site is maintained by the National Library of Medicine (NLM) at the National Institutes of Health (NIH).[133] As Joice explains:

"Specialists in ontology not only work with data and information, they also work with knowledge-domain specialists, forming a nucleus of expertise in the domain to be mapped and formalised, which allows them to structure the data and formalise the relationships and properties across the information captured and create a more formal computational knowledge. This allows them to interrogate databases in an autonomous manner which produces richer forms of knowledge beyond formal classification systems such as taxonomies."

The three movements of Deep Tech are elevation, scaling and amplification. Computational ontologies provide an essential role in enabling these dynamics to be achieved. The journey through these movements starts with Deep Tech Discovery (described in chapter four), a process which is not only focused on developing new innovations by elevating value propositions, but which also has a strategic dimension by aligning the understanding of the objectives, functioning and architecture of digital technology across the whole organisation. Our discovery process has been designed to take an abstract and extensive concept to the point where it becomes a shared vision and focused to the point where a minimum viable product can be developed.

Having developed a hypothesis about how the organisation will deliver value to customers, and having built the first prototypes, it then becomes necessary to enter into a phase of scaling, and this is where an organisation needs to define and understand its core growth capabilities (described in chapter five). But when an organisation attempts to scale, it faces the multiple challenges of alignment, co-ordination, integration between systems, data structuring and applications. The problem is one of semantic fusion. This occurs when people in the same organisation talk about the same things in a different form and different things in the same way. The danger of scaling, therefore, is that it results in fragmented and weak systems which fail, do not integrate and are rigid and inflexible. In these instances, IT systems are developed which are out of alignment with business strategy, goals and objectives. The solution for leaders is to align the organisation's use of language and terminology semantically at every stage of the development of Deep Tech innovation.

A common and difficult problem which organisations face emerges when they wish to develop platform-based digital capabilities and offers. Their technical foundations are normally already well-structured and available, and they usually have a high level of expertise in designing the individual data and applications services. What is commonly missing, though, is the data domains element. The reason is that data domains use 'Ubiquitous Language', a term which Eric Evans created to describe the language which is shared by teams, developers, domain experts and other participants in software development.[134]

Ubiquitous languages are necessary because in each part of an organisation, people refer to the same concepts in different ways. For example, for the finance department, a customer is a person who is registered for billing purposes; for marketing, a customer is a person who is converted into a client through a funnel sales processes; for sales, a client is the person who is purchasing a product or service. So data relating to this same person or entity can signify different things in different data domains. For this reason, problems are experienced when integrating systems due to rigidity in their definitions of the data.

Failure to integrate systems always results in higher costs and project delays. We can think of the problem of integration as each system having its own computational mental model of the data they hold, as well as using different computational languages to process the data and the data structures. Just as people have different cognitive mental models, systems have different metaphorical mental models and their own computational languages which define their domains of data. Our Deep Tech Discovery process integrates organisations' digital operating models with their digital platform architectures by making individual teams' prior silo-based mental models explicit, so that they develop the ability to better understand the impact of any digital systems they introduce across the wider enterprise. Structuring Deep Tech Discovery in this way enables organisations to co-ordinate changes across departments and other potential silos.

Organisations which do not have the requisite level of competency in the design of data domains and business ontologies will always struggle to implement their digital transformation roadmaps and make the shift to digital economy business models supported by Deep Tech platforms. Without this level of competency they suffer from fragmented infrastructures and non-aligned teams and departments. If business leaders do not have the ability to understand technology from a systemic perspective and lack a formally defined computational ontology which takes into account the mental models behind each data domain, the design, development and effective implementation of Deep Tech platforms is simply not possible.

It is normally the case that leaders frame their analytical thinking in terms of the data structures which support their organisations. When leaders understand the computational mental models behind the data structures that constitute the architecture of the enterprise, it then becomes possible to build meaningful new platform architectures which integrate these data structures seamlessly across the enterprise's digital applications.

Not only do Deep Tech leaders need to understand the Ladder of Seeing in relation to the lived experience of those people they wish to understand, empathise and connect with in order to elevate collective intelligence, they also need to understand the ladder in relation to collective human-computer sensemaking. Computers gain knowledge when operating at the level of computational ontologies, and so when these are integrated into human decision-making, the impact and outcome become amplified.

Computational mental models arise through the mental models and cognitive biases of those developers responsible for the software written for artificial intelligence systems. They occur when there is an absence of systemic thinking which is sustained through a fragmented vision of data and domains. Software developers therefore must be fully conscious of these sources of bias which impact on the quality of AI being deployed and the digital architectures which depend on it.

The next level of leadership in amplified organisations is achieved when leaders make the shift from a focus on personal mastery of hard and soft skills to a focus on achieving collective mastery across whole Deep Tech ecosystems. Leaders must therefore understand the way in which systems thinking, lived experience and business and computational mental models all connect together as the foundational drivers of next-generation amplified organisations. This connection across multidisciplinary perspectives is made possible through networked intelligence.

In 1995, Don Tapscott provided a prescient vision of the impact that the internet would have on our lives, focusing on how networked technology would change the way in which individuals and society interact.[135] He would then summarise the path to knowledge transference through the four principles of collaboration, transparency, sharing, and empowerment.[136] With exponential increases in computational power, Geoff Mulgan coined the term 'big mind' to describe human and machine capabilities working together, defining 'collective intelligence' as "the capacity of groups to make good decisions—to choose what to do, and who to do it with—through a combination of human and machine capabilities".

While Mulgan referred to collective intelligence as a capacity, we use the term 'networked intelligence' to refer to both the architecture and the aim of the endeavour to integrate human and computational knowledge and wisdom across networked systems. We therefore define 'networked intelligence' as purposeful architectures, networks and deep collaboration platforms which allow conscious groups of people and ethical ontological-level computational knowledge systems to combine to solve our most difficult economical, social and environmental challenges. These elements are shown schematically in Figure 6.8.

FIGURE 6.8 Networked Intelligence

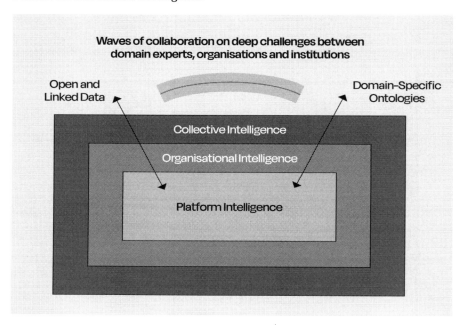

An organisation's digital operating model can be thought of as a digital ecosystem consisting of digital solutions which support formal operational production processes, data networks and the informal political power structures. Figure 6.8 shows the connections between platform intelligence, organisational intelligence and collective intelligence:

Platform Intelligence: Information architectures that transform data into information which is then analysed through artificial intelligence models in order to create knowledge. The result is deep learning models.

Organisational intelligence: The definition, construction and enriching of organisational ontologies through information architectures and the knowledge produced by them.

Collective intelligence: Domain-specific ontologies which are freely available to organisations and researchers through open platforms. They are created through the amalgamation of different organisations' ontologies whose open data sets are anonymised and published so that other entities can make use of the data and collaborate to find solutions.

Platforms utilise data domains, which are aligned and made meaningful through business ontologies. This means that the business capabilities are therefore able to make maximum use of the data domains and the organisation shifts from being data-driven to AI driven. An example of the use of this type of ontology is the BBC which has published the computational ontologies it is using to support its audience-facing applications. The range of ontologies include:

Creative Work Ontology: used to express the minimum metadata necessary to express a piece of creative content in the platform.
Food ontology: a simple vocabulary for describing recipes, ingredients, menus and diets.
Journalism ontology: an ontology which holds classes and properties which are useful for describing the journalistic output of the BBC.
Politics ontology: an ontology which holds classes and properties which are useful for describing the journalistic output of the BBC.
Sport ontology: a simple lightweight ontology for publishing data about competitive sports events.[137]

Advances in Deep Tech have led to the creation of open networked ontologies which have accelerated research and made collective intelligence possible. These ontology platforms allow researchers to browse and filter ontologies, search ontologies using users' own terms, submit new ontologies and explore the mappings between ontologies. One of the most comprehensive examples of collective intelligence is The National Center for Biomedical Ontology whose goal is to support biomedical researchers in their knowledge-intensive work by providing online tools and a web portal. This allows researchers to access, review, and integrate disparate ontological resources across all aspects of biomedical investigation and clinical practice. A major focus of their work involves the use of biomedical ontologies to contribute to the management and analysis of data derived from complex experiments. The centre achieves its objectives by advancing standards of good semantic and software development practice by creating tools and theories that support a wide range of biological and semantic projects, collaborative research activities and end user applications. In this way, laboratories and researchers working on clinical trials around the world are able to collaborate more effectively using collective intelligence.

Not every organisation that collects and stores data is able to make use of it in a meaningful way. Many organisations often spend a fortune on data diagnostics, but then get stuck and are unable to progress to the stage of developing meaningful insights from the diagnostics. These types of data-driven organisation experience a gap that arises due to the quality of data and information held and which blocks them from developing information, knowledge and, ultimately, wisdom (Figure 6.9).

FIGURE 6.9 Data-Driven Organisations

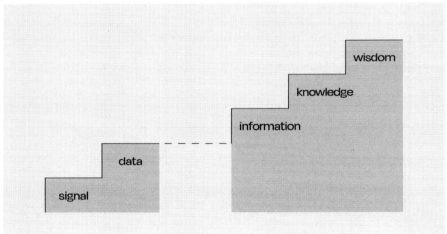

For example, the way in which massive data sets are currently collected and analysed in relation to social networking normally consists of simply counting the frequency of messages, key words and hashtags, etc., which can then be visualised in relatively simple ways.[139] Big data applications and technologies have increased the power of capturing, processing and analysis. But what has not increased is the definition and comprehension of knowledge. Our ability to share and disseminate knowledge is therefore currently restricted.

An ontology helps us to interrogate databases using semantic reasoning, because it is the relationships to other pieces of information that makes a piece of data meaningful. In this way, Tim Berners-Lee's dream of a semantic web can be made a reality, where knowledge is shared, in addition to data and information.

Networked intelligence enables the computational and data resources available in an organisation to become amplified, thereby enabling data to be transformed into explicit knowledge. The aim of computational ontology is to make implicit knowledge explicit. Without ontologies, data is not meaningful; we only have properties and definitions of entities. To demonstrate this point, Joice shared with us one of her projects when 1STi worked with the innovation team from one of Brazil's largest and most important media groups in January 2021.

This project had been created to demonstrate to journalists and technologists inside of the media group the quality and power of insights that can be derived when knowledge graph technology is combined with domain-specific journalism ontologies. In this trial, an ontology was created by recording three one-hour prime-time news programmes on three different channels, one belonging to the media group and two from competitor channels. The data consisted of 160 minutes of content with 137 different speakers identified.

The audio from these recordings was then transcribed and knowledge graphs were created (Figure 6.10). These graphs were able to demonstrate the main themes and content discussed in a visual manner, highlighting the most influential and frequent terms. This enabled the similarities and difference between reporting on the three different networks to be analysed, including the amount of time dedicated to the discussion of each theme.

The knowledge graph had the limitation of not having a definition of the meaning of the connections between elements. For this reason, a journalism ontology was created to complement it. While the knowledge graph showed different *speakers*, it was the ontology which was able to demonstrate individual named *people*, enabling biographical information to be added, thereby enabling a richer and more meaningful analysis. So although knowledge graphs represent networks of knowledge, they lack an explicit semantic and contextual dimension; in other words, they lack meaning and the ability to provide deeper forms of analysis at the semantic level. In this example, the knowledge graph was able to demonstrate that a person gave an interview about education whereas the

FIGURE 6.10 Journalism Domain Knowledge Graph and Ontology

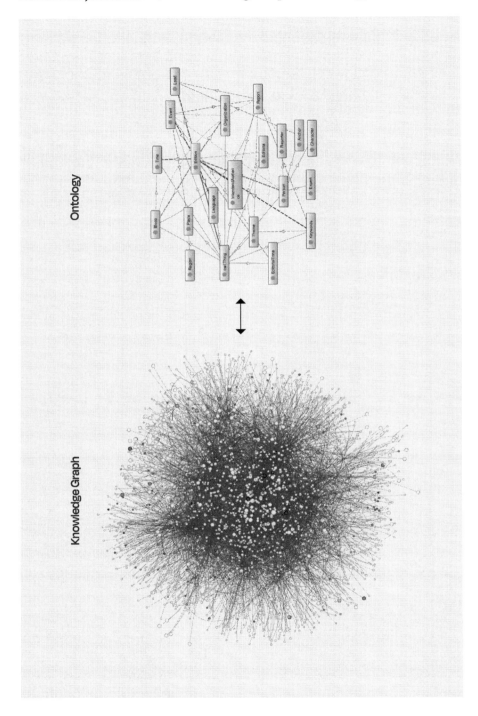

6 · PURPOSE-CENTRED DESIGN

ontology revealed that a particular speaker was an educational expert and senior professor from a specific university research department.

The journalism ontology enabled the media group to analyse their news content against that of their competitors in many new and interesting ways. It enabled them to understand the themes of each news channel which were receiving emphasis, for example, health, politics, national news. This form of ontological analysis has the potential to provide a more transparent form of media analysis of news coverage, allowing researchers to understand the subject matters being covered by news channels, and to what extent and where.

Computers are still unable to work at the level of epistemology in order to create ontologies using artificial intelligence. Ontologies created automatically from knowledge graphs still lack contextual and semantic layers. The human factor in the creation of ontologies is still fundamental. While computers do of course specialise in mathematical forms of analysis, the epistemological dimension of knowledge means that we require interpretative lived experience ontologies such as UMIO's health-focused experience ecosystem described in chapter three.

The term 'sensemaking' was coined by Karl Weick to highlight the importance of having methodologies to make sense of that which is unknown, thereby facilitating our ability for comprehension, understanding, explaining, extrapolation and prediction through structured frameworks.[140] The challenge of sensemaking is that it is an interpretative process in which both cognitive bias and intentional political and power-based manipulation can play a role. The practice of human sensemaking has also not yet managed to accompany the rapid advances in either information systems such as business intelligence and analytics or new socio-technological environments such as social networks, mobile computing, online media and crowdsourcing, etc.[141] Our Deep Tech practices therefore include a process we call 'computational sensemaking'—the uniting of knowledge graphs with computational ontologies, combined with codified lived experience ontologies, to enable organisations to elevate the analyses they carry out on their data bases and data lakes, thereby achieving knowledge at scale.

Current state of the art artificial intelligence systems such as GPT-3 are able to process massive volume of data, and as we have sought to show by including its contributions in this book, the quality can be remarkable. But they still currently lack structures for context and meaning. For this reason, despite having more computational power than a human brain, GPT-3 still commits fundamental errors that people do not. The power of computational ontology is achieved through being the link between data bases and data lakes, information architectures and deep learning models. Philosophical ontological concepts such as lived experience complement computational ontologies, resulting in powerful new forms of deep thinking. Computational sensemaking therefore occurs at the intersection of the deep thinking and deep collaboration pillars of our conception of Deep Tech—the aim of which is the maximisation of purposeful and authentic collaboration between artificial intelligence and human expertise, cognition and decision-making.

The development of computational ontologies is opening up a new frontier of human knowledge. Until now we have depended on human experts for the type of inferential reasoning that has been beyond the capabilities of computers. An expert's ability to reason is limited by their ability to process large amounts of data at the same time. Ontologies enable the scaling of reasoning because they contain the logic of domain-specific knowledge.

The new frontier of artificial intelligence is now deep sensemaking. It is only in this domain that Deep Tech leaders, scientists and designers will solve the problem of *the meaning of meaning*, i.e., developing intelligence that is truly able to know and understand the information that it is processing. When this becomes possible, the internet will transform dramatically, as will the way in which we use applications such as search engines to find, process and understand information in the digital realm. This is the point at which intelligence becomes amplified through Deep Tech (Figure 6.11).

At this present moment, deep learning models are built based on the data that is currently available to them. This approach, for example, has enabled GPT-3 to generate texts of such high quality that it is now extremely difficult to distinguish them from those written by humans. However, data-centric learning models do not consider knowledge structures. In order to make deep learning more powerful, we need to shift from a focus on data to a focus on the nature of the relationships between that data. This is done through networked data and open data hubs.

When this amplified pool of data and information is available to an organisation it can be further enhanced semantically, ensuring that the data now has quantitative, qualitative and textual attributes. This then allows data specialists to elevate up to the next level of deep sensemaking, that of domain ontologies. With domain ontologies in place and more data links available, analysis is no longer just statistical; those people who are analysing the data become able to make more intelligent inferences (reasoner inferences). These are further augmented through openly available scientific research.

FIGURE 6.11 Computational Sensemaking

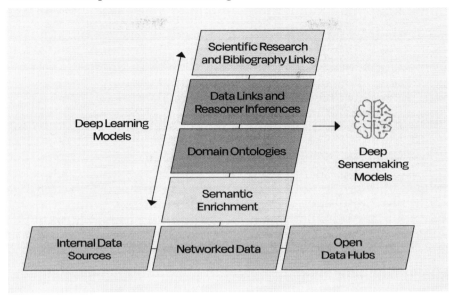

This is the point at which a profound form of deep sensemaking emerges—the highest form of deep collaboration between machines and people.

Executive Summary

→ The purpose of Deep Tech is to contribute to the regeneration and evolution of our social and environmental ecosystems.

→ Purpose-centred design is a way of thinking which helps us to develop technology with soul. This is a concept that helps us to elevate our thinking to a transcendental level of design, where we are able to create technologies which are in service to life and which have the potential to elevate the human condition.

→ Augmented agility is a methodology for digital transformation projects that focuses on the human dimension of agile projects. It is a way of being that allows organisations to reach higher ground.

→ Achieving augmented agility occurs when there is a clear understanding of the mission, vision and values of an organisation. This drives the need for leaders to be able to communicate their vision in a way which inspires and supports people to 'live the mission'. The ethos which underpins augmented agility is to ensure that people are empowered to take ownership of the challenges they face and to learn from mistakes.

→ Computational ontology is the key to unlocking the power of data. It provides the essential foundations for enterprise architectures and digital operating models. It enables organisations to standardise and align complex Deep Tech digital architectures with enterprise goals, objectives and business functions.

→ Open networked ontologies and artificial intelligence models allow organisations to build collective intelligence and share the knowledge they have gained. Deep sensemaking is the point at which human sensemaking meets artificial intelligence.

7

The Impact
of Deep Talent

NEW ECONOMY JOB SKILLS

In 1958, mathematician John von Neumann coined the term 'singularity', a point at which "technological progress will become incomprehensibly rapid and complicated."[142] After his death, his colleague Stanislaw Ulam explained von Neumann's conception of the singularity as "the ever-accelerating progress of technology and changes in the mode of human life which gives the appearance of approaching some essential singularity in the history of the race".[143]

From this moment on, scientists, technologists and futurologists began to contemplate the impact that humanity will experience when computers become more intelligent and smarter than people. However, what is often missing from these conversations is a meaningful discussion of *being*; who we are and humanity's essential nature. For this reason, universal human values are fundamental within our conception of Deep Tech as they provide a basis for understanding our highest essence.

Buddhist economics, unlike neoclassical western economics, provides us with an insightful threefold definition of work. Firstly, work is a means by which it is possible to obtain the resources needed to have a dignified life; secondly, an opportunity to shape the ego and become a better human being when dealing with other people and with situations which are beyond our normal comfort zone; and thirdly, an opportunity to put into practice our unique personal talents for the benefit of others.[144] Work, therefore, is a way for people to achieve happiness by fully exercising their talents, without any limitations or restrictions. Money does of course remain relevant, but as a means and not an end in itself.

The singularity can be framed from both dystopian and utopian perspectives, meaning that technology can be seen as a path to enhance our quality of life, or alternatively, as threat to our very existence. For this reason, in 2018, 1STi, Holonomics and Vai na Web founded the Deep Tech Talks in São Paulo to initiate and facilitate discussions among executives about the future we expect, the future we desire, and the future which we are able to co-create; a possible future where technology has soul.

While it is not possible to predict the mid-term future with great accuracy, what is now becoming clear is the need for people to develop new skills for the new economy. The World Economic Forum's *Future of Jobs Report 2020* maps out the following critical jobs and skills trends of the future:

- Half of all employees will need reskilling by 2025, as technology rapidly evolves;
- Critical thinking and problem-solving skills will grow in prominence in the next five years;
- Self-management is a key emerging skill, as organisations introduce more flexibility and active learning into the workplace.[145]

According to Professor Klaus Schwab and Saadia Zahidi, the technological disruption that is transforming jobs can also provide the key to creating them:

"We find ourselves at a defining moment: the decisions and choices we make today will determine the course of entire generations' lives and livelihoods. We have the tools at our disposal. The bounty of technological innovation which defines our current era can be leveraged to unleash human potential. We have the means to reskill and upskill individuals in unprecedented numbers, to deploy precision safety nets which protect displaced workers from destitution, and to create bespoke maps which orient displaced workers towards the jobs of tomorrow where they will be able to thrive."[146]

In chapter two we examined the way in which Almanaque Digital is helping to develop core skills in the areas of critical thinking, cultural awareness, empathy and citizenship. These skills are very much aligned with the ten most important skills cited by *The Future of Jobs Report* that chief human resources and strategy officers from leading global employers believe are the most important across industries and geographies:

1. Complex problem solving
2. Critical thinking
3. Creativity
4. People management
5. Co-ordinating with others
6. Emotional intelligence
7. Judgement and decision-making
8. Service orientation
9. Negotiation
10. Cognitive flexibility[147]

Our conception of Deep Tech places as much value on people as it does on the technology itself, highlighting the need for organisations to develop deep talent and understand the importance of deep collaboration. Creative solutions to our complex problems will not simply be developed by ever more sophisticated algorithms, but will come from skilled and talented people, able to provide different perspectives on those problems and challenges many different people are facing globally, due to the quality of their deep thinking.

MIND THE GAP

Before organisations can begin to develop deep talent, they first have to overcome three major gaps:

i. The digital knowledge gap
ii. The gender gap
iii. The inequality gap

These three gaps combined are creating major obstacles to organisations being able to achieve their digital transformation ambitions and becoming truly Deep Tech. Organisations who wish to grasp the challenge and search for deep talent from non-traditional backgrounds can amplify their results and impact in a far greater way than they had previously imagined. For this reason, it is important to understand the exact nature of these gaps and how to bridge them.

The Digital Knowledge Gap

The concept of the digital divide has its roots in the knowledge gap research of the 1970s, when communication researchers in the United States began to debate the theory of the increasing 'knowledge gap'. The main hypothesis was that, "Segments of the population with higher socio-economic status tend to acquire information at a faster rate than the lower status segments, so the gap in knowledge between these segments tends to increase rather than decrease."[148] During that decade, research started to explore the manner in which education level and socio-economic status made a difference in acquiring knowledge. This was driven by a concern that increased information would disproportionately favour those who were already advantaged in society, and be at the cost of disadvantaged groups of society, rather than narrowing the gaps between these two groups.[149]

Following the first wave of the internet in the 1990s, this research expanded its scope to explore the digital knowledge gap. As the Organisation for Economic Co-operation and Development noted in 1999, "Visions of a global knowledge-based economy and universal electronic commerce, characterised by the 'death of distance' must be tempered by the reality that half the world's population has never made a telephone call, much less accessed the internet".[150]

In 2001, the OECD defined the digital divide as "the gap between individuals, households, businesses and geographic areas at different socio-economic levels with regard both to their opportunities to access information and communication technologies (ICTs) and their use of the internet for a wide variety of activities".[151] Their research raised the following key questions:

- Where does it occur and why?
- What are its causes?
- What are the relevant parameters?
- What is its extent, that is, how wide is the digital divide?
- Where is it most critical?
- What are its effects likely to be in the short-term?
- In the longer term what needs to be done to alleviate it?

If we look at an advanced economic region such as Europe today, research shows that a large proportion of people still lack basic digital skills. In 2020, the European Commission reported the following findings:

"In 2019, the percentage of people that have at least basic digital skills reached 58% (up from 55% in 2015). A large part of the EU population, however, still lacks basic digital skills, even though most jobs require such skills. In 2018, some 9.1 million people worked as information communications technology (ICT) specialists across the EU, 1.6 million more than 4 years earlier. Nevertheless, there remains a shortage of ICT specialists in the labour market: 64% of large enterprises and 56% of SMEs that recruited ICT specialists during 2018 reported that vacancies for ICT specialists are hard to fill. The problem is even more widespread in Romania and Czechia, where at least 80% of enterprises that either recruited or tried to recruit ICT specialists reported such difficulties. There is also a gender balance issue as only one in six ICT specialists is female. Overall, in the Human Capital dimension of the Digital Economy and Society Index, Finland, Sweden and Estonia are the most advanced."[152]

This lack of basic digital literacy means that business and organisations are still challenged by the digital divide today. While many businesses are now placing digital strategy and data analytics high on their agenda, those which are either weak or have no capabilities in that area will clearly struggle. As we shift into the digital economy, all organisations will become technology companies, and for this reason they have to balance their desire to elevate through innovation with their needs to find, nurture and retain deep talent.

The Gender Gap

Consultant, coach and systems thinker Kimberly Faith is the author of *Your Lion Inside: Discover the Power Within and Live Your Fullest Life*, which she describes as "a manifesto for hope" and a "manual for truth" which was written to help women "be more, do more, and give more" and to help each of us help create a culture that values the contributions of women in both their organisational and personal lives. The way she has achieved this is through creating a series of seven structured archetypes, which she calls "The Sisterhood of Seven", allowing her to reveal deep-seated patterns of thinking and behaviour which are often extremely difficult to perceive in ourselves when we lack the wisdom and guidance necessary to help us break out of our old habits.

Kimberly's purpose is to provide new tools and stories to endow women with the power, strength and hope necessary to allow them to shift into new ways of thinking and to live confident lives, where they are using all of their potential for the greater good of everyone. Her focus, therefore, is on helping women understand the unseen narratives that are holding them back. The first step in her process is to expand women's awareness. The metaphor she describes is of taking women out of their fishbowl:

> "Awareness is the first step in seeing the world differently...Awareness plucks you out of the fishbowl, shakes you off, and sets you down next to it, allowing you to see clearly for the first time. When your perspective changes, everything begins to shift."[153]

Globally, women held just 29% of senior leadership positions in 2020. And in the US, almost thirteen Fortune 500 companies were run by men for every company run by a woman.[154] Kimberly's desire is to fully empower women, and this involves a mental shift from a victimhood mindset to a focus on the stories of the future and the power that women have now:

> "It is about our misperceptions that distort what we see in the mirror every day. Has the time come for us to consider that the glass ceiling is also a mirror? By this, I mean that it is time for us to look at ourselves in the mirror and see that there are specific beliefs, assumptions and internal mindsets also standing in our way. These mindsets don't show up in the new workplace surveys because many women themselves don't even realise that the mindsets are standing in the way. Why? It is unconscious, and the Narrative has convinced us otherwise."[155]

When we look at digital skills in the workplace, businesses and organisations are currently not managing to achieve parity between women and men. According to the European Commission's *2020 Women in Digital (WiD) Scoreboard*, women are still less likely to have specialist digital skills and to work in the digital field compared to men, with only 18% of information and communications technology specialists in the European Union being women.[156]

As the World Economic Forum explains: "Gender parity has a fundamental bearing on whether or not economies and societies thrive. Developing and deploying one-half of the world's available talent has a huge bearing on the growth, competitiveness and future-readiness of economies and businesses worldwide".[157] The report concludes that not only are women still not being represented in management or senior leadership positions, and not only are they not achieving parity with men in relation to digital skills, women's participation in the wider labour market has stalled and financial disparities are increasing. Globally, there is a deteriorating trend in emerging and developing economies, and this is offsetting the gains made in OECD countries.[158]

The WEF highlights three primary reasons for this:

i.   women have greater representation in roles that are being automated;
ii.   not enough women are entering professions where wage growth is the most pronounced; and
iii. women face the perennial problem of insufficient care infrastructure and access to capital.[159]

Their report suggests that policy-makers need to take action to better equip younger generations, particularly in developing nations, with the skills to succeed in the world of future jobs. Increasing formal education attainment is necessary but it is insufficient to provide both young women and men graduating from every level of education with the types of skills needed for the digital economy's job market. In this respect, gender gaps remain, and are likely to become exacerbated unless addressed now.

The Diversity Gap

The World Economic Forum's Diversity, Equity and Inclusion 4.0 report defines diversity as "the range of human differences and variations, whether they are inherent (by birth) or acquired (by experience)".[160] These variations can results in different forms of exclusion and discrimination in the workplace. The report lists a range of characteristics of people who are at risk of experiencing discrimination, including age and generation, gender and gender expression, sexual orientation, race, ethnicity, religion and social origin.[161]

We are now experiencing a convergence of three major social and economic trends:

i.   the accelerated use of advanced technologies;
ii. job market disruptions to both remote work and work requiring physical presence; and
iii. a call for greater inclusivity, equity and social justice.

These trends represent a major opportunity for businesses and organisations to re-evaluate their current performance in relation to diversity, equality and inclusion. The reason is that future economic opportunities will require higher levels of creativity and innovation if businesses are to realise the best use of new technologies. It is clear that diverse and inclusive workplaces can contribute considerably to achieving this vision.

As the WEF's *Diversity, Equity and Inclusion 4.0* research shows, companies leading their geography and industry for diversity, equity, inclusion and belonging perform better than their market average across a wide range of key performance metrics.[162] On the other hand, companies that fall behind their peers in diversity, equity and inclusion experience a competitiveness penalty, being 29% less likely to achieve above-average profitability than their market mean.[163]

Many companies are struggling to fill their digital and IT vacancies while also wishing to address their diversity and inclusion gaps. The solution we have developed for our Deep Tech ecosystem is to look for, nurture and support talented young people from non-traditional educational backgrounds, including the development of deep talent from disadvantaged communities in many cities in Brazil. The way in which this has been achieved in a systemic manner with positive social impact is explained in the following section.

SOCIAL IMPACT AS A SERVICE

While technology is providing the means for organisations to create new hybrid forms of work where people spend time both in the workplace and at home, the social landscape is also changing people's attitudes to leadership and organisational culture. This is happening in parallel with a heightened focus on how organisations are performing in relationship to their ecological, social and governance standards (ESG). We believe that when the desire is authentic, businesses have a pivotal role to play not only in terms of committing to ESG objectives, but in creating genuine impact by developing an inclusive form of capitalism.

This attitude can be seen in the open letter that Larry Fink wrote to CEOs in January 2021.[164] Fink is an American billionaire and chairman and CEO of BlackRock, an American multinational investment management corporation. With nearly USD 8.7 trillion in assets under management as of December 31, 2020, BlackRock is the biggest investment management company in the world.[165] Fink positioned climate change as the key theme of his annual letter, while also writing about the need for organisations to consider their talent strategies from a sustainability perspective:

"I cannot recall a time where it has been more important for companies to respond to the needs of their stakeholders. We are at a moment of tremendous economic pain. We are also at a historic crossroads on the path to racial justice, one that cannot be solved without leadership from companies. A company that does not seek to benefit from the full spectrum of human talent is weaker for it; less likely to hire the best talent, less likely to reflect the needs of its customers and the communities where it operates, and less likely to outperform.

"While issues of race and ethnicity vary greatly across the world, we expect companies in all countries to have a talent strategy that allows them to draw on the fullest set of talent possible. As you issue sustainability reports, we ask that your disclosures on talent strategy fully reflect your long-term plans to improve diversity, equity, and inclusion, as appropriate by region. We hold ourselves to this same standard."[166]

As a social entrepreneur from Rio de Janeiro, Igor founded 1STi based on his understanding of the challenges facing young talented people from the favelas of the city wishing to have a career in IT. His overriding mission is to develop ecosystemic solutions which overcome inequalities through the development of new and innovative business models that give vocational training and career support to young adults who were previously excluded from IT. He knew from the very start that founding 1STi would be a major opportunity to put his ambitions into action.

The first favela in Brazil appeared in Rio in Janeiro in the late nineteenth century built, by soldiers who had nowhere to live following the War of Canudos. Following the abolition of slavery, many of the poorest and most disadvantaged citizens began to move in, creating a trend for informal low-income settlements far from urban centres, which expanded in the 1970s when people left rural areas to seek work in cities.[167] Favelas have now become known as communities, in an attempt to remove the stigma of this form of built environment.

Research from UNESCO shows that 13.6 million people are living in communities in Brazil.[168] To gain some perspective on just how large this population is, if this population were a state, it would be the fifth largest in the country. And if all of Brazil's communities were a country, it would be larger than the size of Portugal, which has 10.3 million inhabitants, and Belgium, with 11.6 million inhabitants.[169] While Brazil has a population consisting of 55% black people, in favelas the population is 67%.[170] 44% of households in favelas are headed up by women, higher than the national average.[171]

The state of Rio de Janeiro has more than 10 percent of the population living in favelas. When questioned about what this population saw as being most the important issues for the future of the country, 40% of people cited health and 36% cited education as needing to be developed.[172] And in relation to technology, 50% of inhabitants own a computer while 86% have a mobile phone.[173]

The scale of this level of inequality, discrimination and social exclusion shows that solutions can only truly have impact if they are systemic in nature. A number of social and economic trends are now converging together which signal the reinvention of businesses through the opportunity of deep talent. As Peter Evans, Managing Partner at the Platform Strategy Institute, puts it, "Talent has become the new frontier of the platform economy".[174]

As one of the four pillars of our conception of Deep Tech, deep talent amplifies the deep thinking in organisations by continually providing new voices with fresh perspectives on problems and challenges, giving them the ability to find systemic solutions that meet many different people's needs, and not just a small segment of society. Figure 7.1 demonstrates the way in which we can explore the social impact landscape.

The schematic of the social impact landscape is based on an organic metaphor of cultivation to highlight the systemic nature of solutions that enable organisations to authentically meet their ESG operational obligations. For this to take place, organisations need to shift from thinking about people in relation to a war for talent to an understanding of how they can nurture deep talent. Understanding the social impact landscape therefore starts by understanding the roots of the context, which relate to the economic and business environment.

Research shows that while on the surface trees may compete for sunlight, underground they may work in a collaborative manner by forming resource-sharing networks, sharing nutrients via root grafts and developing the resilience to overcome environmental challenges.[175] In the same manner, organisations flourish when provided with the right nutrients from the environment, and this in turn leads to social and environmental health. The relationship is systemic since just as organisms require water from precipitation to provide moisture for soil, which regulates the quality of terrestrial groundwater, organisations are embedded in wider social and environmental ecosystems which provide the conditions for them to grow and prosper.[176]

FIGURE 7.1 Social Impact Landscape

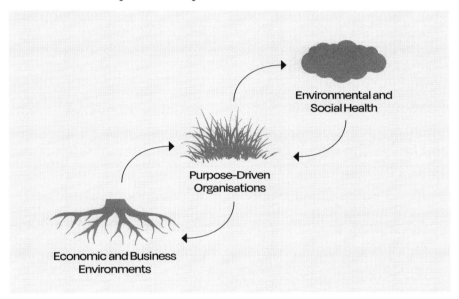

Social Impact as a Service (SIAAS) is an innovative business model developed by Vai na Web, the Rio de Janeiro-based initiative which we introduced in chapter two. Inspired by their systemic conception of social impact, Vai na Web develops and runs technology learning journeys for young and talented individuals, training and empowering them to be able to fully take part in the Deep Tech revolution. Aline Fróes is the co-founder of 1STi and co-founder of Vai na Web, which began life in 2014. For Aline, Vai na Web is an effective way for organisations to fill their skills gaps:

"Tim Berners-Lee was the great inspiration for Vai na Web. We need diversity in our thinking to solve our key social, economic and environmental problems, because diversity brings creativity and advancement. Companies always say they need skilled people and that one of their main challenges is the loss of their most talented people. In many communities meanwhile, there are so many young people who are interested in technology. So Vai na Web emerged to act as a bridge between the energy of young people who want to learn and evolve and the business world. While companies mainly search for talent from the world's top universities, we are showing them that there are deeply talented people to be found on the fringes. Bridging the gap between organisations and deep talent can be incredibly empowering."

Vai na Web is a high-tech and social impact movement that expands human capabilities and re-qualifies the workforce to face the challenges of the future of work. As Aline explains:

"Favelas are full of energy, diversity, culture, creativity and ideas. These are highly desirable characteristics for businesses. Vai na Web is creating a hotbed of digital talent. Technology doesn't ask what your age is or what your gender is, it challenges you every day, like a sphinx, to decipher it. Our mission therefore is to help companies fulfil their dreams of innovating, of having more diversity, and of having brilliant people contributing and developing; people who are chasing after their life's dream."

The initiative is more than just a training and recruitment programme for young people:

"The way we work is through what we call the talent pipeline. When our students join, they spend six months in our school learning a wide range of IT and programming skills such as HTML5, CSS3, Javascript ES6 and many others. Those who pass then have the opportunity to join Vai na Web's design studio in order to gain practical experience. Once they have gained a year of experience working on and delivering real projects, developing a high level of technical excellence, we then support them in finding employment in IT companies."

The logic of Vai na Web's Social Impact as a Service business model is shown in Figure 7.2. It was created to deliver benefit to both clients of Vai na Web and the social environment where that organisation is located. Vai na Web achieves this by delivering an inclusive form of education for students from disadvantaged backgrounds through the delivery of IT services. These are cost-effective because students who are working on commercial projects through Vai na Web's talent pipeline also receive guidance and mentoring from 1STi and experts from the wider Deep Tech Network, thereby guaranteeing high quality design work for clients.

FIGURE 7.2 Social Impact as a Service in Vai na Web

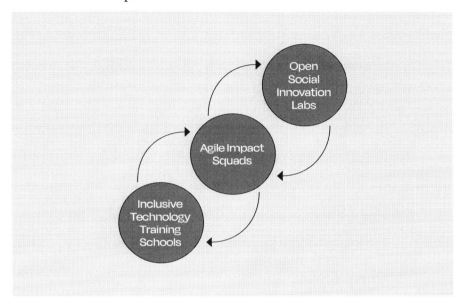

Social Impact as a Service builds on the shared value business model, first introduced in 2011 by Michael Porter and Mark Kramer, who defined three variations: re-conceiving products and markets, redefining productivity in the value chain and building supportive industry clusters at the company's locations.[177] By taking a systemic perspective, SIAAS helps organisations collectively achieve their ESG goals who would otherwise struggle to implement an authentic initiative on their own. During the period in which an organisation is receiving this service, they are contributing to the advancement of education through schools which are developing the next generation of programmers.

SIAAS improves society by taking young adults out of potentially violent life paths by providing them with structured career opportunities. Families who would not normally have the means to provide an education become able to support their children with this programme. This allows the overall talent pool in an economy to grow, meaning that rather than organisations becoming stuck in the metaphor of the "war for talent",[178] they are able to shift into an understanding of the role they are able to play in supporting talented young adults from non-traditional educational backgrounds.

Vai na Web is therefore a primary example of our conception of deep collaboration, where deeply talented individuals work on deep challenges which business and society are facing. When students first graduate from Vai na Web, they are invited to join small software development squads which focus on projects which deliver social impact, an example being Almanaque Digital (described in chapter two). Companies investing in SIAAS enable Vai na Web to expand these squads into their Open Social Innovation Lab, which is where clients, institutions and Vai na Web researchers collaborate together on social technologies. The aim of this lab is to conceive new elevated value propositions, platform solutions and networked business models which are based on collaborative ecosystems of stakeholders. When these projects reach fruition, Vai na Web is then able to invest in further squads which generate additional investment resources, resulting in more schools and more qualified young IT experts.

Desirée Queiroz is an economist specialising in local development and the United Nation's sustainable development goals. She is also the executive director of Precisa Ser, a networked social innovation institute founded by 1STi which helps leaders and sponsors of social projects create positive impact. She explains that Vai na Web is "an initiative that can be considered an accelerator of the sustainable development goals (SGDs) by allowing us to transform the world without ever leaving anyone behind. This is because Vai na Web provides an integrated way to meet the goals. The first goal that we meet is the fourth, quality education, which in turn leads to the eighth, access to income, which then positively impacts on poverty eradication, (goal 1), industry, innovation and infrastructure, (goal 9), and reduced inequalities, (goal 10)".

Central to the success of Vai na Web has been the involvement of Zoraide Gomes, who is better known as Cris dos Prazeres, meaning 'Cris who is from the Prazeres community'. Cris has played a critical role in the community of Morro dos Prazeres in Rio de Janeiro for more than twenty years, founding many different organisations and initiatives to improve education, health, recycling and women's rights, in addition to championing the teaching of advanced technology and human development. As Cris explains, technology can be empowering in a country with such high levels of inequality:

"The digital illiteracy rate is huge in Brazil. So thinking about new ways of sharing knowledge in the area of technology could potentially be a very productive and prosperous path for the country as a whole. Although digital technology is bringing disruption, there is also an associated social contract based on solidarity which can help us overcome our challenges. Technology can bring a more human dimension, because people now of all ages are using it, from children to people of retirement age. What we need to do is make technology more accessible, so it can connect people and become more understandable for those using it."

Cris sees the success of Vai na Web as not only due to the teaching of new technology, but really understanding the lived experience of those young adults who may not initially be receptive or interested in furthering their education:

"Everyone at Vai na Web works hard to ensure that people are not labelled or excluded. We really need to be able to perceive the potential power of young people for our initiative to fulfil its potential. We took a long time to listen to young people in our community to understand how we could help them become digital natives, thereby making the very best use of technology which serves real social needs. So one of the foundations of our philosophy is that we need to believe in our youth and believe in the professional power that our youth possess. We believe in our reality, our future and technology at the service of humanity. We don't just teach technology, therefore, we form graduates with professional and personal skills so that they will be happier in their lives, no matter which area they may end up working."

Yago Dos Santos Cambinda is a graduate of Vai na Web who is, at the time of writing, an intern at IBM, and who is studying information systems at university. His experience of Vai na Web is a testimony to that which Aline, Cris, Desirée and the team are achieving. As Yago explained:

"In addition to technical knowledge, there is the development of social skills. This training covers areas such as how we should treat each other, how we can work together effectively, and was one of the things that helped me the most as a person. As a young apprentice, a company is not looking for someone with a lot of knowledge, but with a willingness to learn, and that's where

Vai na Web made a total difference. This is what companies are looking for. Technology is for people; it isn't machine for machine, but machine for humans. It is essential to develop social-emotional skills. Every programmer is an entrepreneur, always looking to solve a problem. This is what being an entrepreneur means. Vai na Web also really helped me with this aspect, putting me in contact with many entrepreneurs."

Cris sees Vai na Web as being a platform for which a digital education is not only one of the development of technical skills, but of development of the whole person as well. For her, Vai na Web is about "realising our collective dreams, thinking together with young people, dreaming together with young people. There is a place that is still far away for many of our country's youth, and that is to believe. But we can believe in the creation of a better world; believing not only in yourself, but in networking, believing in other people and in their abilities".

Chris is expressing the fundamental essence of the philosophy of Deep Tech in which the focus is on the elevation of everyone. She continually emphasises the central role of families within the community, meaning that pedagogical practice of Vai na Web explicitly mobilises and involves family members who may not have previously had a family member enter into higher education, an aspect which helps students to develop self-esteem and the courage to learn. As Cris puts it:

"Vai na Web is a mix of excitement, commitment, professionalism and the desire to dream collectively. We have the capacity to dream and to renew our dreams every day. And technology is the tool by which we realise and materialise these dreams. Our students learn the power of dreaming. To learn to program with us is a flight plan where the sky will never be the limit. Technology is a very important path, and it is a human path, one of great respect. That is why it is important that companies increasingly recognise this place of youth and their enthusiastic ability to support transformation within an organisation.

"Vai na Web has a vision of abundance, in which everyone has space, trust and love. The best teacher in the world is the one who shares information, because when they share, they also learn. Our vision is one of technology at the service of society. We transform the world through technology."

Executive Summary

→ Deep Tech is a new vision of technology, business, leadership, work and life, where deep technology is based on universal human values and deeply integrated into society. Deep Tech is a new way of being, where technology is not a barrier, but an opportunity to develop our full potential in work, leisure, health and education.

→ The digital knowledge gap is the disparity between those who have the skills and knowledge to leverage the digital economy and those who do not.

→ Diversity in technology and innovation is important to companies to stay competitive. Having a more diverse workforce can help companies innovate more and achieve better business results. At the end of the day, the tech industry will not find a way to make more women feel welcome or comfortable in the workplace until it is made clear that this is an issue that the business community as a whole is serious about addressing.

→ The social impact landscape is a systemic approach to understanding the social impact contexts of business. It is based on the organic metaphor of cultivation to highlight the systemic nature of solutions that will enable organisations to authentically meet their ESG obligations. For this to take place, organisations will need to shift from thinking about people in relation to a war for talent to understanding how they can nurture deep talent.

→ Vai na Web is an initiative which is transforming the lives of young adults from vulnerable communities in Brazil by giving them the opportunity to learn how to code and to develop their technology and people skills as professionals.

8

The Quality of our Relationships

SEPARATION AND DISCONNECTION

Building on the philosophy of many thinkers, starting with Karl Marx, who fore-saw the role knowledge would play in production, in 1993, Peter Drucker present-ed a vision of the world in which a new era was emerging that would impact the world economy. This would be the *knowledge society*, an era based on the distinc-tive characteristics of humans to create and innovate, thereby generating com-petitive value for organisations.[179] This vision predicted the rise of the knowledge worker and a world of work where machines were servant to people. Despite all of the advances the knowledge society has generated, it has not allowed us to solve many complex problems and to raise humanity to a higher level of prosperity and equality, contrary to Drucker's observation that "rich people...have almost ceased to matter".[180]

For this to happen, we need to make the shift from the knowledge society to a new age of wisdom. What is now required is an expansion of our consciousness and the embodied living of universal human values. We believe that we now have a great opportunity to expand our awareness and perception of ourselves and of the purpose of our existence, providing the opportunity to improve the way we manage resources and create a new qualitative form of value that is ever more inclusive and which brings prosperity for all.

One possible answer to the question of how we can progress towards the age of wisdom can be found in the observation of nature and in the four and a half billion years of Earth's existence.[181] Neil deGrasse Tyson, a scientist who revived and updated the Cosmos series (originally written and narrated by planetary scientist and astrophysicist Carl Sagan), reminds us that the past has a lot to tell us about our future:

"In one respect, we're ahead of the people of Ancient Mesopotamia. Unlike them, we understand what's happening to our world. For example, we're pumping greenhouse gasses into our atmosphere at a rate not seen on Earth for a million years. And the scientific consensus is that we're destabilising our climate. Yet our civilisation seems to be in the grip of denial; a kind of paralysis. There's a disconnect between what we know and what we do. Being able to adapt our behaviour to challenges is as good a definition of intelligence as any I know."[182]

When we shift our thinking from human civilisations to the natural world, we find many different ways in which the animal kingdom uses technology for survival and protection. As we described in chapter six, it really does become possible to think of technology as being a part of nature. So, for example, termites build mud towers which are able to regulate heat; ants have colonies to grow fungi in their gardens; and birds use twigs, branches and pieces of wood to build their nests.

An important question for we as humanity to ask is do we see technology as part of nature, or do we see technology as separate and disconnected from nature? A number of existing studies already point to this disconnection between people and nature, and people and other people. For example, in 2021, Earth Overshoot Day fell on the 29th of July.[183] This day marks the date when humanity has exhausted nature's budget for the year. This means that for the rest of the year, we are maintaining our ecological deficit by drawing down local resource stocks and accumulating carbon dioxide in the atmosphere.

A second indicator of our disconnection is the global levels of poverty and income inequality. The most recent figures from the World Bank estimate that 9.2% of the world population (689 million people) lived below the International Poverty Line (IPL) in 2017. More than 60% of the world's poorest people live in

Sub-Saharan Africa, which at 41% has the highest regional poverty rate. Around a quarter of the world's population (24.1%; 1,811 million people) live on less than $3.20/day, while almost half (43.6%; 3,271 million people) live on less than $5.50/day.[184]

We define sustainability as 'the quality of our relationships' and these statistics relate to a low collective quality of the relationships with our environment, a low quality in our relationships with other people and a low quality in the relationship we have with ourselves.[185] When we become disconnected, we move away from all that is natural to us—our abilities to be resilient, to survive and to be present and mindful in the environment. When we disconnect from nature, we start to experience major problems, no longer living together in a healthy and evolving manner. For this reason, Deep Tech is a way of being in which we reconnect with ourselves, with other people and with the wholeness and livingness of life.

RELATIONSHIPS AND EMPATHY IN HUMAN NETWORKS

In February 2019, Apple announced Deirdre O'Brien as their senior vice president of Retail + People. This new role was designed to expand her responsibility for people-related functions in Apple to one of leading the company's global retail reach, focusing on the connection between the customer and the people and processes that serve them. Commenting on the new appointment, Apple's CEO Tim Cook commented that, "At Apple, we believe our soul is our people, and Deirdre understands the qualities and strengths of our team better than anyone".[186]

The phrase 'employee experience' is credited to Dr Kaveh Abhari who began to notice in 2007 that brands which delivered exceptional customer experiences were those that invested the most heavily in their employees. He also discovered that positive customer experiences also impact on more positive employee experiences, due to employees deriving more meaning from their work.[187] Just as the customer experience is the sum total of all the experiences that a customer or client has with an organisation, the employee experience is the sum total of their experiences with their employer during their time at that particular organisation. HR departments that consciously manage the employee experience do so by dividing it up into five key stages—recruitment, onboarding, development, retention and exit. Their effectiveness lies not just in the way in which these organisations take a more holistic view of the careers, engagement and experience of their employees, but also in the way in which HR departments understand the contribution of technology on employee experience, performance and retention.

HR teams therefore have a key role to play in their organisation's strategy by ensuring that employees have the right technology, information and advanced analytical tools available to do their jobs, as well as working more closely with IT departments to ensure better alignment in digital transformation programs.[188] Within our framing of Deep Tech, the role of HR professionals expands, therefore, to playing a pro-active role in Deep Tech Discovery development, contributing, along with the leadership, to the alignment and communication of strategic goals and initiatives, and using their expertise in psychology and the humanities to develop mastery of lived experience in the areas of design and leadership.

It is not possible to implement a major organisation-wide digital transformation initiative without taking into account the human dimension. Digital transformation and cultural transformation are two sides of the same coin. For this reason, we propose that HR fundamentally transforms from being primarily an operational department to one of central strategic importance, just as it has at Apple. By taking responsibility for the introduction and living of human values, HR can impact even more significantly by helping people to flourish and contribute to the development of the amplified organisation's capacity for reinvention and adaptation, enhancing collective creativity, systemic thinking, collaboration and communication.

Any digital transformation programme has to be fundamentally concerned with the networks of people who will be impacted by the changes, applications and platforms being proposed. The way we improve the quality of our networked relationships is through the constant practice of empathy, understanding others in their unique attributes, lived experience and life stories. As we saw in chapter two, the universal human values express who we are as human beings and are the basis for sustainable and high quality relationships. They are universal in that they form the ethical basis of every grouping of people—families, communities and organisations, for example—as they allow us to connect, communicate and interact in a collective and harmonious way in order to achieve our common goals. When the values are present in an organisation, authentic dialogue becomes possible, allowing teams and groups to overcome complex problems, even during times of great change.

Sustainable relationships therefore are the ones in which all relationships receive attention and care, taking into consideration their uniqueness. Change processes are successful when we do not seek to move other people, but when we seek to move our *relationships* with other people. Enhancing the quality of relationships in our networks helps us to expand our understanding of resilience, an essential quality, especially when change processes hit their more challenging moments. When we get to know each other and interact based on human values, we are better able to pass through changes, difficulties and adversities in a more active and safer way. Resilience is more than just an individual quality; it is also a collective attribute which emerges as a result of high quality relationships between individuals.

It is interesting to note that natural systems possess this systemic quality of resilience, which affords survival and evolution. An example can be found in the lifecycle of an amoeba called slime mould.[189] This living being is a fascinating organism to study since it has two distinctive phases in its lifecycle. When food is plentiful, in the form of bacteria, this species exists as independent free-living amoeba. However, as soon as food becomes scarce, something quite extraordinary happens; the previously independent amoeba begin to act as a coherent whole. After a few hours, some of the amoeba begin to aggregate around cells which act as centres which send out chemical signals (Figure 8.1).[190]

FIGURE 8.1 Slime Mould Aggregation

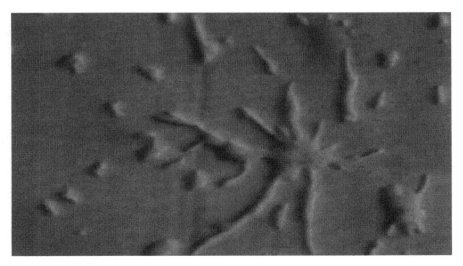

Around each centre several thousand cells will amalgamate and start to form a new multicellular organism. Previously identical cells will begin to differentiate into specific cell types, forming a fruiting body (Figure 8.2). This new organism consists of a base, a stalk which rises up from the base and a fruiting body made up of a ball of live spores. This new being does not need as much food in this format because each individual has 'transformed' into a new type of organ and requires less food to survive.

FIGURE 8.2 Slime Mould Fruiting Body

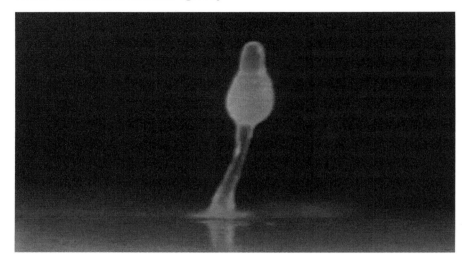

When the food is abundant again in the environment, the organism separates and the amoebas once again become free and independent individuals. To ensure survival, the slime mould turns into a new being able to overcome changes in the environment, i.e., periods of food shortages, demonstrating a high quality of relationship that results in collective resilience. This behaviour of slime mould has inspired the design of more resilient management systems within human organisations. One example is the Amoeba Management System created by Japanese executive Kazuo Inamori, founder of Kyocera.[191] This system was created to bring out the best in people in those moments in which solutions to new problems need to be found. People from every part of the organisation come together temporarily to find the solution to a problem, and after achieving the result, they separate.

We can draw some important lessons from the behaviour of slime mould by noting a number of key characteristics such as:

• Faced with the change in the external environment and the need for collective response, the system self-organises, based on the 'trust' between individuals;

- Information flows freely throughout the system;
- In times of scarcity the individual entities are able to undergo a rapid transformation;
- New structures emerge in a way in which cannot be determined simply by a study of the individual parts. A cell transforms into a new type of cell and takes on new functions;
- All cells contribute to the success of the community.

When we think of organisations as living systems, our perspective changes to one where we can contemplate the world as interconnected, interdependent and self-organising. John Bonner, an American biologist who studied slime mould for many decades, said that we still have a huge amount to learn from this humble form of life. Some of his original video footage can be seen in his original slime mould movies on Youtube.[192] Having watched this footage, it is interesting to then ask these following questions:

- Why in times of change or difficulties are people not able to act like slime mould?
- Under what conditions can the behaviour of slime mould occur in our human systems and interactions?
- Which are the situational human values necessary for systemic resilience to occur?

Sometimes one of the barriers to having high-quality relationships is the diffi-culty we have in understanding the way in which other people's experience of life is qualitatively different to that of our own. We tend to see other people from our own life context, and when we fail to expand this view, we end up judging behaviours and attitudes in a way that is often incomplete. We understand that people may have different opinions, but it is not clear to us that these differences are based on stories and experiences which are very different to ours. For this reason, actively working with the concept of lived experience can be powerful and transformative.

In order for us to expand our vision and develop the type of systemic resilience seen in the behaviour of slime mould we need to practice empathy. There can be occasions and contexts where people are not able to spontaneously or nat-urally practice empathy, especially during times of change in an organisation when many unknown factors may be contributing to a general sense of fear and stress. What we need to do is to find a way for us to reflect on how each of us understands and qualifies the relationships with everything that is around us, including technology.

The way in which we can do this is to first start by creating a relationship map to help us think beyond those colleagues, teams and people with whom we work most closely, and towards our wider networks of friends, families, colleagues, acquaintances and also people not yet known but who we would like to know and have a connection with (Figure 8.3). Relationship mapping allows us to create a visual picture of those relationships that are important to us and which will help us grow and develop on our professional and personal journeys. By mapping these relationships it becomes possible to identify those areas requiring improvement and the type of action needed.

FIGURE 8.3 Relationship Map

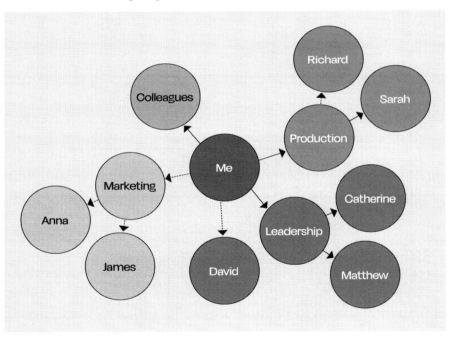

The general concept of a relationship map is to use each connection to spur new ideas. Drawing these maps reveals the quality of our relationships and the level of care we have with each of the people represented. The exercise enables people to deepen and strengthen their relationships with a few simple changes to their routines and behaviours.

Relationship maps are created by placing your name in a circle in the middle of a blank sheet of paper. Circles are then added around yours and labelled with the names of people, companies, allies, customers, vendors, associations, etc., that are important to your success. In some instances these can be people or entities who you do not yet know but with whom you would like to start a relationship. A line is then drawn between you and the person/entity to represent your relationship with them. A solid line represents a strong relationship, a dotted line represents a relationship in place but which needs strengthening, and no line represents a relationship which needs to be cultivated. With practice, relationship maps can become more detailed in their structure, helping people to understand and explore more complex scenarios.

After drawing a relationship map, the following questions can then be asked:

• What are the important relationships needed to achieve my professional and life goals?
• What do I need to do to strengthen my existing relationships?
• What do I need to do to start relationships that are important but not yet in place?
• What can I do practically in order that my relationships have an even higher quality?

Relationship maps can also be used as a tool to support conversations between leaders and members of their teams, providing clarity around the relations that each person has. The maps also facilitate discussions about how teams can act to improve the quality of their work and design projects, and for this to be really effective, they must be driven with an empathic understanding of the needs and ways of seeing of those taking part in the conversation.

To help teams develop a deep understanding and empathy for other people, Dave Gray created the empathy map.[193] It has been used in many different contexts, such as learning more about the needs, attitudes and opinions of clients, improving the customer experience and better understanding the people and mental models present in an organisation in order to develop teams, design work environments and improve the employee experience.

One of the great challenges with the practice of empathy is that people often assume that the way they perceive and experience reality is exactly the same as other people. The power of the map lies in the way it structures different issues relating to how people think and feel about particular situations, ones which will often be perceived in markedly different ways. In times of change and

FIGURE 8.4 Empathy Map Canvas

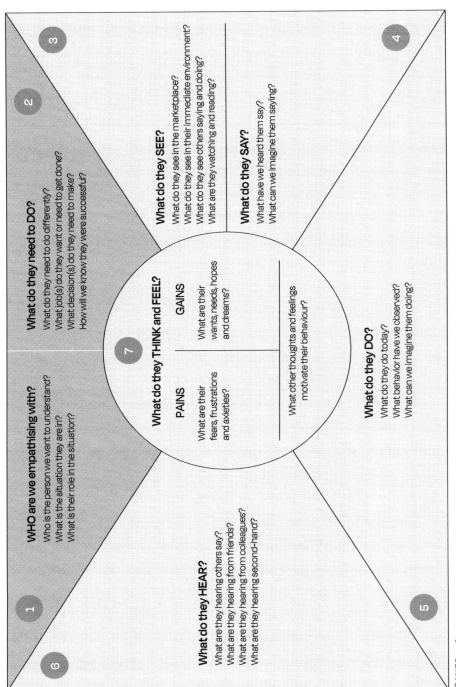

WHO are we empathising with?
Who is the person we want to understand?
What is the situation they are in?
What is their role in the situation?

What do they need to DO?
What do they need to do differently?
What job(s) do they want or need to get done?
What decision(s) do they need to make?
How will we know they were successful?

What do they SEE?
What do they see in the marketplace?
What do they see in their immediate environment?
What do they see others saying and doing?
What are they watching and reading?

What do they SAY?
What have we heard them say?
What can we imagine them saying?

What do they THINK and FEEL?

PAINS
What are their fears, frustrations and axieties?

GAINS
What are their wants, needs, hopes and dreams?

What other thoughts and feelings motivate their behaviour?

What do they DO?
What do they do today?
What behavior have we observed?
What can we imagine them doing?

What do they HEAR?
What are they hearing others say?
What are they hearing from friends?
What are they hearing from colleagues?
What are they hearing second-hand?

©2017 Dave Gray

transformation, the practice of empathy becomes even more relevant. The reason is that in the context of uncertainty, people often close up and do not express how they are feeling out of fear or anxiety, and this may harm their individual performance and that of their entire team as well.

Like any tool, there are guidelines for how the empathy map can best be utilised. Gray explains how to work with the empathy map in the following manner:

1. Start with the GOAL section, by defining who will be the subject of the Empathy Map and their goal: something they need to DO. This should be framed in terms of an observable behaviour.

2. Once you have clarified the goal, work your way clockwise around the canvas, until you have covered SEEING, SAYING, DOING, and HEARING. The reason for this is that the process of focusing on observable phenomena (things that people see, say, do and hear) is like walking a mile in their shoes. It gives us a chance to imagine what their experience might be like, to give us a sense of what it "feels like to be them".

3. Only after you have made the circuit of outside elements do you focus on what's going on inside their head, one of the most important aspects of the map's design. The main idea is to imagine what it's like to be inside someone else's head. That was and is the primary power of the mapping exercise.[194]

Empathy mapping is a central process for the ideation and design of Deep Tech solutions as well as in the management of people. It is therefore one of the most fundamental tools for both customer experience and employee experience design. Its effectiveness comes through providing a structured framework to explore the different questions necessary to construct as complete a picture as possible about the thoughts, feelings and actions of those people in our immediate spheres.

Having completed an empathy map and reflected on the feelings and thoughts that influence the person's behaviour, a plan of action can then be constructed based on what was observed in the map. This allows leaders, for example, to define the best way to address the anxieties, fears and learning objectives of their team members, thereby strengthening relationships.

When carrying out this exercise in empathy, designers and leaders are able to clearly understand the pains and issues which people experience, rather than trying to minimise the issues. Every journey of change starts with self-knowledge. Before we can learn to lead, inspire and engage other people, we must first learn how to help ourselves, and for that we need self-knowledge.

SELF-KNOWLEDGE

It is not normally common for people in organisations to be encouraged to take the time out from their busy work schedules to contemplate and understand how the many challenging situations they have experienced in life have impacted their lives, such as the first time moving home, city or country, the loss of loved ones or a significant change in career. In a corporate environment it is even rarer to have the time and space to stop and reflect together on our personal life stories, how we have become the people we are today and the paths we have taken. When we do dedicate time to focus on our personal journeys, the results can be positive and extremely rewarding. We come to recognise our strengths and those areas that require improvement, and we become the protagonists of our stories in a more conscious manner.

While challenging us, this process of self-knowledge also captivates us. Many films that touch us emotionally are those which present a hero in conflict with themselves, or a character who finds themselves in a challenging situation at the start of their story. In some films, the identity of the protagonist is defined by the quality of discipline as they develop self-knowledge, such as in Star Wars, with the central character Luke Skywalker who is trained by the master Yoda. Other films present main characters who discover unexpected qualities within themselves in times of need and change.

Each one of us is unique and has our own way of seeing things, a window through which we see the world. This 'window' is in fact the mental model with which we understand reality. The concept 'mental model' refers to the structures, paradigms, ideas, assumptions and beliefs that we construct when reasoning about situations and accepting or rejecting conclusions. According to Philip Johnson-Laird, "Each mental model represents a possibility, capturing what is common to the different ways in which the possibility could occur".[195] They are the result of our education and experience of life. As each one of us has our own story of learning, each of us makes a different and individual 'reading' of reality, seeing the world through our own individual windows. The characteristics of each window are unique to each person and are larger or smaller depending on the amount of knowledge and experience learned.

Cognitive studies have demonstrated that our mental models can limit the quality of our reasoning, due to the fact that people do not seek counterexamples to their mental models as a matter of course. Marco Ragni and Markus Knauff, for example, obtained evidence to support their theoretical assumption that people have a preference for simple mental models and typically only construct one rather than multiple mental models with which to test their assumptions and deductive reasoning.[196]

When we become aware of how our mental models impact on how we see the world, we are able to understand ourselves better, knowing that we cannot 'see' the totality of things. We are better prepared to listen to others—people who have a different 'window' to ours and who can therefore complement us. This enables us to develop more humility, understanding that we need to broaden our view of situations, contexts and people before evaluating a situation and reaching conclusions about them.

Bruce Lee wrote extensively on the theme of self-knowledge. He studied Kung Fu in Hong Kong under the legendary master Yip Man. While he is most famous for his television and film career which lasted for seven years, he also studied philosophy at the University of Washington.

From a young age Lee wrote prodigiously on a number of topics which attracted his interest. His ideas helped energise his life and career and made it possible for him to live a happy and assured life, overcoming challenging obstacles with seeming ease. Lee died in 1973 at the age of 32. It was not until 2000 that the book *Striking Thoughts: Bruce Lee's Wisdom for Daily Living* was published, covering seventy topics such as achievement, adversity, overcoming challenges, success and personal liberation.[197] We conclude this chapter with insights and inspiration which come from some of Lee's most striking thoughts on self-knowledge, and how they relate to Deep Tech projects and transformation initiatives.

1) Self-knowledge involves relationship

Working with empathy and relationship mapping in various long-term change programmes enables people to develop empathy and a deeper awareness about the impact of their unconscious body language and behaviours on others, while also helping them to recognise the emotional needs of others during times of organisational transformation.

2) Criticising others is easier than coming to know yourself

Digital and cultural transformation programmes need to provide space for people to practice dialogue. When conversations become heated, emotional and confrontational, people may try to impose their thoughts without thinking. When we deepen our level of self-knowledge we develop the ability to ask someone why they think the way they do rather than to automatically oppose them in order to 'win'.

3) True seeing leads to new discovery and uncovering our potentiality

When we practice genuine dialogue we are able to consciously take ourselves away from just seeing from our own perspective in order to think better about the point of view of others. The ability to participate in dialogue at this level is a powerful ability for technology designers, experience designers and leaders to possess.

4) Dependency on others for esteem reduces self-sufficiency

When we develop an authentic degree of self-esteem, we are better able to focus on the job in hand, rather than losing time and energy attempting to find approval from others. This does not mean acting without care or respect for others. Self-esteem is an example of universal human values in practice.

5) Self-knowledge is true mastery

Before we can overcome our external challenges and achieve all of the goals which we have, we need to look inside ourselves. When we have this inner calm, analyse situations more accurately and make sense of what is happening, we can inspire people around us.

In the following chapter we will examine personal mastery and how it relates to the consciousness design practices of Deep Tech.

Executive Summary

→ The way we see the world is based on our lived experience. In order to improve our relationships and system resilience, we must become aware of the many unique life stories and lived experiences of the people around us, and seek to understand them.

→ The concept of lived experience is closely related to the concept of empathy, which is the ability to understand and share the feelings of others. Empathy is a capacity that is essential to human relationships. It is the ability to step into other people's shoes and to recognise their perspective. It is the capacity to understand the other person's point of view and to experience their feelings. Empathy is a vital quality in the relationships which we have with others, and also a necessary quality in the relationship we have with ourselves.

→ The HR department has a key role to play in the employee experience, and the employee experience has a key role to play in the customer experience. The strategic role of the HR department is changing in the digital age. HR departments are no longer just responsible for recruitment, training, staff development and employee relations, they are also responsible, together with leaders, for the employee experience—the sum total of all the interactions that an employee has with their employer.

→ The power of empathy is that it allows us to understand the perspective of others. It is an essential tool in the design of Deep Tech solutions and in the management of people.

→ Self-knowledge is fundamental to the conscious design practices of Deep Tech. It is the first step to understanding others, to have empathy for others, to serve others and to inspire others.

The Collective Mastery of Deep Tech

THE EVOLUTION OF DESIGN THINKING

We define 'design' as intentional creation through artistic and technical skills. Our approach to designing Deep Tech always includes thinking about our lived experience of technology and its impact on both the material well being of people as well as the impact on our inner lives.

In the last twenty years, design thinking has become popular as a way to inject more creative thinking and innovation into organisations which were not previously design-led. The emphasis is on developing a multi-disciplinary approach which brings people together from different backgrounds to solve business and organisational problems using the same processes that traditional designers have always used in the development of products and services such as cars, electrical appliances, computer systems, etc.

All variants of design thinking embody the same principles which were first described by Nobel Prize laureate Herbert Simon in *The Sciences of the Artificial* in 1969. One example is the popular five-phase model proposed by the Hasso Plattner Institute of Design at Stanford:

Empathise – with your users

Define – your users' needs, their problem and your insights

Ideate – by challenging assumptions and creating ideas for innovative solutions

Prototype – to start creating solutions

Test – solutions[198]

One of the major misconceptions with design thinking has been the way in which it has been reduced to a singular methodology, meaning that the thinking in design thinking has become lost. For this reason, as we saw in chapter four, our Deep Tech Discovery phase in design projects involves an educational component to expand people's understandings of core Deep Tech concepts, in addition to a multi-disciplinary exploration of the problem space. We therefore use a more nuanced definition of design thinking with three interconnected dimensions:

1. An innovation mindset that understands the value of design;
2. A design approach that is democratic and involves people who are not designers;
3. A collection of methodologies and tools used in the design of products and services that are used in the search for solutions to complex problems in all types of organisation.

When seen from this more expanded perspective, it is easier to appreciate the positive impact which can be achieved by working with design thinking as a methodology. User experience designer and researcher Shane Ketterman has outlined the key benefits for businesses and organisations:

Inclusivity: democratic processes close the gap between designers and users, helping to create diverse solutions;

Understanding: designers aim to discover the real causes of the problems;

Different voices: the inclusion of people from different backgrounds in brainstorming sessions to increase creativity;

Reduced risk: questioning the problem, questioning assumptions and questioning the implications.[199]

In recent years, design thinking as a practice has received criticism due to the way in which the objective of inclusivity is often not authentically achieved. Other criticisms focus on the way in which there can be a lack of systemic thinking in arriving at solutions. Many conscious designers are exploring the way in which design thinking can evolve to become genuinely inclusive.

Creative Reaction Lab, for example, has pioneered Equity-Centred Community Design, a creative problem solving framework based on "equity, humility-building, integrating history and healing practices, addressing power dynamics, and co-creating with the community".[200] As they point out in their theory of change: "According to the US Census Bureau, by 2050, Black and Latinx communities will make up almost 40% of the United States population, many of whom are currently youth. Yet, these communities face disproportionate racial and health inequities that limit social, economic, and cultural growth. While Black and Latinx youth want to improve well-being for themselves and their families, friends, communities and culture, they currently feel unheard, unsupported, or excluded from opportunities to amplify their power and work toward liberation".[201]

For this reason, their design approach focuses on both the mindset involved and the lived experience of those they are seeking to help:

"When we speak about Equity-Centred Community Design and support its integration into peoples' practice, we are very intentional in stating that we are promoting a mindset shift rather than process adoption. While early integration might look like checking boxes on a to-do list, to truly centre equity and lived experience in daily practice we need to get to a place where questions about power, inclusion, identity, and equity are consistently present in our minds."[202]

Creative Reaction Lab's approach highlights the importance that worldviews play in helping to make the process of design genuinely more inclusive. Design thinking is now evolving to integrate systems thinking practices and principles, without the need to think of them as separate disciplines with separate communities.

Sarah Gibbons, Nielsen Norman Group's Chief Designer, explains the design thinking process in terms of a framework which follows an overall flow of i) understand, ii) explore and iii) materialise (Figure 9.1).[203] Since the design thinking process is iterative and non-linear, Gibbons defines six phases within these larger flows: empathise, define, ideate, prototype, test and implement.

One of the major challenges that organisations face is how to structure their customer-centric innovation teams, departments and labs, etc. Gibbon's schematic is important for the way in which it extends typical design thinking models to include a final stage focusing on the materialisation and implementation of that which has been ideated and tested. When design thinking is seen as a function of an innovation department, the risk is that an organisation's investment in design thinking is focused mainly in the ideation stage, with projects never becoming implemented. The reason for this is often due to a failure to socialise the purpose of design thinking initiatives and engage those people and departments who have a stake in their implementation, launch and success.

FIGURE 9.1 The Design Thinking Process

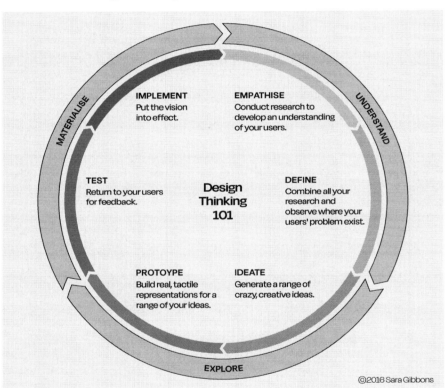

©2016 Sara Gibbons

The question of where to locate design thinking expertise is critical for any organisation due to the four ways in which design thinking can fail to achieve its full potential:

1.   Design thinking takes place in an organisation's research and design

department without any involvement from either business development or product marketing representatives. In these instances, no matter how good the quality of the research is, it will fail to find a commercial sponsor.

2.   Design thinking takes place with involvement from commercial and product teams, but then fails to achieve a proper handover to those responsible for product and customer lifecycle management. In these instances, the insights may not be communicated properly, and of course there are always political issues such as the not-invented-here syndrome.

3.   Design thinking is not managed by someone who is fully qualified in design. In these instances, members of an organisation may take part in design thinking workshops which generate a lot of energy and excitement, but then no actual real design learning takes place which is effectively integrated into the organisational culture because of the level of superficiality of the workshop.

4.   Design thinking is utilised in some form of Deep Tech project, but due to the novelty and complexity of the new concepts being introduced, the initiative fails to achieve either alignment around the qualification of core terms or agreement on the purpose and value proposition.

As an unnamed head of the Industrial Engineering Department of Yale University (and not Einstein) said in the middle of the 1960s, "If I had only one hour to solve a problem, I would spend up to two-thirds of that hour in attempting to define what the problem is."[204] Discovery phases of Deep Tech design projects must be adequately resourced and supported, with time dedicated to both studying the problem and helping non-specialist team members understand the issues under investigation as fully as possible. And as we have continually emphasised, discovery must be fully aligned with the strategy map and elevated value proposition.

There are two main ways in which an organisation can manage these challenges. One option is to create a central design resource who ideate, design and then handover at some point to product management. An alternative is to locate certain design professionals inside commercial and product management teams, and to ensure that these people have formal product lifecycle, customer lifecycle, and profit and loss responsibilities. There is no right or wrong answer, and much depends on the context, but getting this question right means that design thinking and its philosophy and practices permeate more deeply and widely into the culture of the organisation and that it has a more profound impact on the core activities.

The term 'design thinking' was not coined as the result of a new discipline, but rather as a way to describe the various approaches to user-centred design that were being developed in various research centres around the world and which of course were very much part of the continuum of the evolution of decades of design practice. In the mid-90s, Simon, along with a number of his colleagues in the Human Factors department at British Telecom's research and development centre, developed a process they termed 'designing the customer experience' which was created to reposition Human Factors and user-centred design at the very heart of the product life-cycle within organisations, thus helping to lay the groundwork for the development of design thinking, service design, customer journey mapping and concepts such as customer success.

In 1995, Simon and Mike Atyeo published the paper *Delivering Competitive Edge*, in which they succinctly described the benefits that come from the more profound approach to exploring problem spaces that designers follow:

"In response to rapid technological change and increased global competition, service industries have undergone radical change. These were initially focused on reducing cost and time to market, but more recently have concentrated on ways of understanding and anticipating customer needs. We have adopted an approach we call 'designing the customer experience'. At its heart is a programme of research into human needs. By bringing together Marketing and Human Factors with more radical perspectives such as semiotics and anthropology, creative and visualisation skills, and rapid technological advances, we have generated an environment for user-centred innovation."[205]

Here we reach the very heart of design thinking, which is the use of radically different ways knowing the world which comes from years of design practice informed by philosophies which are based on different ways of seeing, observing and comprehending that which is being investigated. As we shift into the digital economy and the development and application of Deep Tech, concepts such as lived experience and artistic consciousness, if fully understood, become integrated into ever-evolving design thinking processes.

Organisations that only take on board the methodologies of design thinking and not its underlying theoretical foundations and mindset often do not manage to evolve their cultures to ones in which design is genuinely integrated into an organisation's practices, rituals and values. Within our Deep Tech Design methodology we facilitate the type of experiences and contact with users, customers and stakeholder communities that can take non-design focused executives from the intellectual to the embodied, thereby allowing them to elevate their understanding of user design practices and the lived experiences of their customers and stakeholders.

While many business leaders are quite able to appreciate the role of technical skills in design, it is still rare to find an appreciation of artistic consciousness in organisations. When we develop artistic consciousness as designers, we develop an ability not only to design using qualitative and quantitative research methodologies, but also to use what we have termed 'philosophical creativity'—the ability to explore multiple scientific paradigms at the same time in order to more fully explore the problem space.

As we saw in chapter six, our Deep Tech design methodologies and frameworks that we have developed all incorporate an ontological level. These practices connect formally-structured computational ontologies with lived experience descriptions codified through methodologies such as interpretative phenomenological analysis.[206] To work at an ontological level is to work at the level of being, of what things are, and this is where personal mastery within design lies.

A designer achieves personal mastery when that which is designed reveals new worlds and new ways of being. Deep Tech is not just about its functionality, it is also about how it can help us to develop new ways of seeing. This is what makes it truly profound, rather than highly advanced or complex. We need transformational mental models to open us to new levels of creative thinking. The masterful use of art can help people to do so by asking new questions, taking us into different lived experiences and revealing meanings and interpretations previously not familiar to us.

One example of how this can work is the way in which we integrated artistic investigations into the presentation of the Deep Tech Podcast hosted by Maria and Igor which launched in May 2020. The podcast was created to help business leaders understand the many different ways in which our Deep Tech ecosystem was conceiving, designing and implementing Deep Tech projects. To achieve this, Igor Postiga, Director of Art and Design at 1STi, teamed up with artist Guilherme Gerais and visual designer Rafael Fontoura to explore the way in which art could be used to articulate and represent many of the new concepts being introduced throughout the series of podcasts. As Igor explained to us:

"Rather than produce one singular visual identity, the project resulted in the creation of a whole collection of vibrant and provocative three-dimensional organic images which captured the notion of representing multiple perspectives, and not just one single take on Deep Tech. Our artistic idea was to reveal the hidden connections which would not normally be recognised, helping people to develop a more open stance by creating works of art that invited open, rather than closed, forms of questioning."

Art is a way in which we can learn to accept the world in new ways, ones of reconnection and interconnection, using all four ways of knowing: thinking, feeling, sensing and intuition. Art and design are therefore pathways in which we can find equilibrium between them, mindfully working in all four modalities, taking us away from homogeneity and into an experience of organic textures, exploring paradoxes and contradictions. This is design operating at the highest levels of artistry, strategy and personal mastery.

Martin Heidegger's warning of the dangers of an obsession with technology was published in 1954. His essay, *The Question Concerning Technology*, ends with the final reflection:

"Thus questioning, we bear witness to the crisis that in our sheer preoccupation with technology we do not yet experience the coming to presence of technology, that in our sheer aesthetic-mindedness we no longer guard and preserve the coming to presence of art. Yet the more questioningly we ponder the essence of technology, the more mysterious the essence of art becomes. The closer we come to the danger, the more brightly do the ways into the saving power begin to shine and the more questioning we become. For questioning is the piety of thought."[207]

Through our Deep Tech ecosystem, we are developing new forms of partnership with organisations who wish to learn how to use purpose-centred design to implement Deep Tech solutions which produce meaningful impact in the world. This is achieved through the development of personal mastery in design, customer experience, platforms, strategy and universal human values. Our network is not simply developing technical skills, we are also creating new ways of being, new ways of working together and asking which new leadership skills will make sense in the context of Deep Tech. Our approach is to discover new forms of creativity in order to help open up new horizons for people and organisations, and we are doing this by allowing our philosophical creativity to inform our practice through new ways of exploring the world and asking qualitatively new questions.

The new generation of leaders in organisations can be thought of as guardians of collective mastery. The power of any network comes through the quality of relationships; it is not about the quality of single nodes in the network, or single individuals who may be highly talented but who do not have the ability to act within a network.

The next generation of leaders will require an ability to develop not just higher levels of design mastery in themselves, but also an ability to develop collective mastery within their organisations and ecosystems. This means developing new rituals, a higher quality of culture and understanding the organisation as a living system, as a dynamic whole. By being guardians of collective mastery, new leaders who understand and work with design will have the ability to use their inherent creativity to design and offer something extraordinary, opening up new horizons to their customers, stakeholders and society.

ARTICULATING THE NEW 4PS THROUGH ARTISTIC CONSCIOUSNESS

In chapter three we explored the role that lived experience can play in finding more humanised solutions to our global problems. Philosophical creativity can provide a crucial new dimension to discovering new insights and ways of seeing, complementing developments in advanced technologies. Rather than artificial intelligence removing the human factor in Deep Tech innovation, the idea is that it will complement the personal mastery of the new generation of Deep Tech designers, technologists and leaders.

In *Customer Experiences with Soul: A New Era in Design*, Maria and Simon describe how the Holonomics Approach can be applied to the area of customer experience design.[208] The phrase 'customer experiences with soul' was created in order to express the essential way in which it is no longer enough for an organisation to have a stated purpose; it also needs to be in touch with its soul, a soul which collectively expresses itself through each part. Soul has to be authentic; it is not a quality which is added on to an existing experience as an additional component.

If an organisation's purpose is revealed to be inauthentic, consumers, activists and pressure groups will eventually find out. Young energetic purpose-driven entrepreneurs who capture the world's attention by embodying soul can find that once their startups reach exponential levels of growth, if lost for some reason, soul can be one of the most difficult attributes to recover.

The journey from where we are now to developing customer experiences with soul starts with ourselves and our relationships with those immediately around us. If we can comprehend, understand and heal these broken and inauthentic relationships, then we can start to rediscover what it means to genuinely share and co-create, whatever we are attempting to envision, innovate and bring into this world.

FIGURE 9.2 The Holonomic Circle

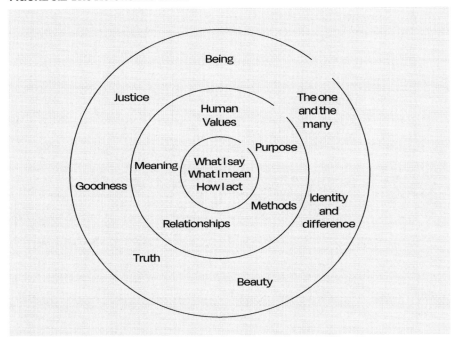

The Holonomic Circle lies at the heart of *Customer Experiences with Soul* (Figure 9.2). It provides a framework for designers, entrepreneurs, leaders and teams to explore together the qualities of soul in organisations in all its dimensions. At the centre is the Trinity, which is where authenticity is expressed as the maximum coherence between what a person says, what they mean, and what they do. The Trinity equally applies to any group, team, organisation, business or ecosystem. Coherence is a quality which can run throughout whole organisations, both internally and externally, and across supply chains, business ecosystems and the communities with which a person or entity interacts. We encounter counterfeit purposes when what a person or group says, means and does fail to coalesce as an authentic whole.

The middle level of the Holonomic Circle helps us to think about those factors which underlie our tools and techniques, and understand why they sometimes work and why at times they do not. This dimension is about exploring the foundations of the tools and techniques being used in business today, and seeing which principles need to be operating in order that they become more effective.

The outer circle contains the Transcendentals, a guiding set of interwoven ideas which we can use to explore and talk about our products, services and customer experience. If we are to truly understand customer experiences and understand how people are interpreting our products, services and brands, we need to explore the way in which language and reality belong together—how we participate in reality and interpret the world. The 'truth' is something we can never definitively arrive at, due to the limitations of language. But through authentic dialogue, humility and an expanded level of consciousness, we can remain open to an ever changing vista of viewpoints and interpretations where beauty, truth, goodness and justice all belong together.

The Holonomic Circle was used as a template which guided the writing of the Deep Tech manifesto. It articulates the foundations of the deep thinking of Deep Tech in a structured manner, and can be applied in many different contexts such as customer experience design, branding, purposeful leadership, employee experience design, strategy, and cultural and digital transformation. In addition to our own work, it is now being adopted by a number of leading customer experience designers and organisations, in addition to being included in a number of masters and doctoral programmes in the United States and United Kingdom.

The term 'deep thinking' conveys both a sense of intellectual mastery and artistic consciousness. It is these two faculties fully working together which produce the power of the results achieved. For this reason, one of the most profound uses of the Holonomic Circle has been in the work of visual storyteller Paulo Fabre, a Brazilian creative business consultant and internationally recognised photographer.[209] Ever since graduating in Business Administration in 2002, Paulo has always believed in the transformative power of organisations, understanding them as living organisms with those achieving long-term success being the ones that are true to their principles and values. We spoke to Paulo to hear about the way in which he has integrated the Holonomic Circle into his purpose-driven Visual Stories methodology:

"In that era when I was young, having recently graduated and full of dreams, I gained a lot of experience across many different industries while working for a consultancy. I learned to recognise that the true identity of a company is made up of the stories of those who built it and those who work there. In many cases, the real identity is quite different from the straplines they may use in their advertising."

While Paulo still fully believed in the transformative power of organisations, he began to feel that he was not achieving his dream of really being able to make a personal impact. For this reason, in his early thirties, he decided to focus on what had just been a hobby, moving to New York to study photography. He still undertook various consulting projects in this period of transition, but on his return to the corporate world he discovered that there was in fact a way in which the worlds of art and business could cohabit in the same space:

"Deciding to put both on the same page, I started to think and design a way to unite them into a single service. I already knew the importance that storytelling has, and that doing it in an authentic and truthful way can be an interesting strategy to hold attention and connect a message to an audience. We live in an age where on the one hand there is such a wealth of information and on the other there is a poverty of attention. In order to attract and retain people's attention, it is therefore necessary to offer relevant and interesting content in a way in which the audience recognises their own story in the content shown."

Wishing to find a way to differentiate his more artistic approach to business consultancy, Paulo was inspired by the potential he saw in the Holonomic Circle:

"I believe in art as a way of touching the human soul and revealing the truth for its beauty. The penny finally dropped after studying *Customer Experiences with Soul*, highlighting how important it is for brands and companies to locate the elements that make up their soul at the centre of their decision-making. A business book that deals with the soul is revolutionary to say the least. With its dynamic understanding of the relationship between the whole and the parts in a system—customers, employees, shareholders, society, environment, competitors, suppliers—it is possible to see how all are integrated and connected in a greater ecosystem. My mission is to make these links visible and tangible, telling stories, giving contours to the soul of brands."

Through exploring the Holonomic Circle in all its depth, Paulo came to develop a new Visual Stories methodology, a creative process that helps brands to look at their own purpose and establish authentic and true communication processes for their internal and external audiences which he describes in the following way:

> "To be effective, I developed my methodology to help me dive deeply in order to capture the most relevant and pertinent stories in an organisation—just as a diver finds the pearls— bringing the essence, the DNA of a brand, to the surface. In the first stage, I use the Holonomic Circle to identify key elements that constitute the purpose of a brand and also understand its history, its trajectory and align expectations.

> "I adapted the circle by converting it into a canvas, and through design thinking dynamics, I am able to create a great mind map. This map serves as a guide to develop a visual, artistic and textual narrative and guides me to search for the most relevant stories. My delivery is an authentic, exclusive and personalised bank of photographic images of people within an organisation that reflects the essence of a brand and its current moment. I also write a poetic text, the brand manifesto, that serves as a basis for the development of different types of communication in social media, the making of the brand book and also the basis for positioning and repositioning the brand."

During the development phase of his methodology, Paulo met Estúdio Nume, a boutique design, branding and communication agency specialising in brand creation and management. Following this meeting, Estúdio Nume presented Paulo's work to one of their clients, Donatelli, a Brazilian fabric design company founded in 1943, which was restructuring its branding.[210] While Donatelli has been developing fabrics both in Brazil and abroad for over seventy five years, they had begun to invest in innovation, in the form of LAB Donatelli, a new service devision whose purpose is to transform their customers' wishes into unique designs, such as custom-made curtains and pillows or the renovation of a piece of furniture, which are designed and made by experienced craftsmen.

Donatelli were looking to expand their brand beyond its traditional audience to new younger customers with interests in art, culture and design. In order to discover insights as to how to communicate these new concepts to their audience in a clear and structured way, Paulo started a process of immersion in the history of the brand, understanding its legacy, its current context and its trajectory. Paulo facilitated three design thinking sessions in which the questions he asked led to the completion of the Holonomic Circle canvas. These sessions were attended by Donatelli's senior leadership team including Paula Coussirat, Director of LAB Donatelli; Deny Barbosa, commercial director and leader of the brand repositioning process; and the partners of Estúdio Nume, Paula Paron and Maurício Albuquerque.

Paula Coussirat began working in the Donatelli factory from the age of twenty, having inherited a passion for both creating and seeking ever new ways to satisfy the needs of customers from one of her aunts. It was therefore interesting to hear her describe the experience of developing a new brand narrative with Paulo and Estúdio Nume through the framing of the Holonomic Circle:

"There was no clarity about what we had been doing. The most valuable part of the process was delivered without realising it during the discovery phase. Each curtain or pillow carries a story of passion, legacy, dedication and involvement and which we hadn't realised. Filling in the Holonomic Circle brought awareness about important elements of our brand that, being intangible, had previously ended up being left out. Seeing all of the words on the canvas really made an impression on me. This work was carried out in such a sensitive and skilful way that it revealed riches, skills and values that I had not even known were in me."

Paulo used the Holonomic Circle to bring different people connected to the brand's daily life together, making it possible to share their different opinions and reflect collectively on the qualities of purpose, universal human values, relationships, meaning, identity, truth, beauty, justice and being. Based on the group's understanding of each of these elements on the canvas, Paulo was able to construct a unified narrative for Donatelli through reaching clear definitions of the elements of the circle.

He followed the entire end-to-end process of developing a product, starting with a customer's order arrival at the office, moving on to the ateliers that make pillows, special embroidery, curtains and tapestry, and ending with a delivery. For

Donatelli's designers, the customer story is the starting point and greatest source of inspiration. The second phase of the project was for Paulo and Estúdio Nume to create a brand book which would be written to articulate the essence of LAB Donatelli. In order to do so, Paulo embarked on an immersive photographic study capturing the daily lived experiences of their craftspeople, guided the mind map that he had built from the Holonomic Circle, giving him an artistic appreciation of how LAB Donatelli's purpose is expressed by their people:

> "At the time of photographing, my focus was adjusted to see harmony—that intrinsic beauty when crafting an object with love—and the sparkle in the eyes that a craftsperson has when they see their work progressing."

From these photography sessions, a comprehensive and complete image bank was delivered to be used in Donatelli's social media and other communication channels. Along with Paulo's text, which was written in the form of a manifesto, Estúdio Nume then designed the brand book to assist Donatelli in their brand definition processes. As Paula Paron explained: "The Holonomic Circle was an important guide for Estúdio Nume, enabling the entire brand to be mapped, something that Donatelli had never previously experienced. It worked like a compass. Through the Visual Stories methodology we were able to build a conceptual foundation of words, and from there, develop the communication and branding."

Deny Barbosa is the third generation in his family to work for Donatelli. Accompanying his parents since he was a child, he grew up involved in the company culture. Today, in addition to being their commercial and marketing director, he leads the process of repositioning the brand. It was through working with Paulo's Visual Stories process that he came to realise how many rich and meaningful elements of the essence of Donatelli had remained hidden from the brand:

> "Before this work, our purpose and story were very intrinsic, meaning that we knew about the existence of our culture and our values, but as we had not articulated them in our conversations, they had not become externalised, they had remained hidden. We had taken seventy-five years to build our story of values and purpose, but as we had not paid attention, we had not been able to articulate them to our customers.

"After we carried out the exercise with the Holonomic Circle, a very wide field of perception opened up for Donatelli. This included the history of the company and the way it was built, especially with regard to the character of the family and the way in which we learn and educate ourselves. This process opened our eyes and brought all these values to light, something which was so important, with the external perspective helping us and being of enormous value to the company."

From the perspective of a creative brand agency, Maurício Albuquerque believes that the Visual Stories process was able to take Estúdio Nume to "a higher level of relationship" with their client, creating a deep connection of values and purpose that goes beyond a traditional commercial partnership relationship:

"The Holonomic Circle helped us to really get to know our client better, align our values and bringing us even closer to them. We had a lot of raw branding material to work with, serving as a basis for us to do the redesign and repositioning of the brand. Paulo's photographic image bank and the manifesto resulted in many month's worth of material for social media posts, changing the level of reach and impressions on Instagram, and generating engagement due to the way in which he created empathy in the audience by capturing the lived experiences of the craftspeople. I remember the way, for example, in which people identified with the photographic story of Angela, a seamstress who learned the craft of sewing at a young age, and who is now one of the main partners of LAB Donatelli."

In addition to the objective results of this project—the raw material for posts, visual elements for the website, social media and branding—the immersion provided by the Holonomic Circle and the stories photographed allowed Donatelli to be able to discover and articulate fundamental feelings within the organisation and strengthen the quality of the relationships across the company's production chain. As Paula Coussirat explained to us: "This whole discovery process brought me greater confidence to strengthen alliances, an immense gratitude for the people who transmitted and taught me what I know, respect for those who skilfully execute each item we sell and the responsibility to transmit and perpetuate what I have learned and received".

As we showed in chapter four, the definition of an organisation's elevated value proposition starts with their current value proposition which is then amplified through the lenses of their organisational values, future-fit vision and appreciation of regenerative and sustainable practices. It is the elevated value proposition that articulates the fundamental essence of an organisation by stating exactly how that organisation benefits the lives of customers and wider stakeholders. Due to its central importance, time is required in the discovery phase of Deep Tech projects to collectively define the base proposition and then ideate in order to reach the elevated value proposition. The care and attention shown by Donatelli in their profound journey of discovery and their sensitivity to the lived experience of all the craftspeople who contribute to their success shows just how much methodologies informed by artistic consciousness and philosophical creativity can contribute to this process of uncovering new forms of value and the articulation and communication of an organisation's soul and essence.

THE JOURNEY TO COLLECTIVE MASTERY

When we founded our Deep Tech ecosystem, many conversations emerged discussing those questions that are sometimes forgotten in times of perceived normality. These are questions such as "Who are we?", "What is our proposal in the world?" and "How can our actions contribute to a better world?" This level of personal reflection enables us to rethink how we see ourselves, how we see other people and how we make sense of all that is around us. Our explorations also include the question of the contribution of technology, being both a tool of great power and a reflection of our own beliefs.

For Ricardo Razuk, philosopher and chief financial officer of 1STi, the problem of technology is not technology itself, rather it is what is guiding advances in technology, principally the values of the free market:

"Looking at the history of humanity, we see that people, despite having philosophy, religion and various concepts of spirituality, which all teach us to be prudent, end up not being very prudent at all in practice. Discussions about the potential of new technologies, especially biotechnology, can create a very big shock for people, due to their limitless possibilities, including the possibility of practically creating a human being. We have reached a point of developing a huge technological capacity while our capacity for reflection remains underdeveloped".

This level of philosophical reflection is of fundamental importance in our approach to Deep Tech because it allows us to ask new and highly practical design questions, for example "What is the impact of the use and adoption of new technology on our sense of who we are?" One example is the exponential growth of social networking and the way in which the selfie has changed how we think about ourselves and how we choose to represent ourselves to others. By making these questions explicit, we are able to explore the dangers of technology being used to condition us as humans without us even noticing. Facebook's choice of algorithms, for example, can change what we see on Facebook and from whom, and this in turn can impact on our emotions, attitudes and opinions.[211]

Ravi Venkatesan is an Indian business executive and venture capitalist who in the past was the chairman of Microsoft India and who is currently chairman of the board of the Bank of Baroda, co-chairman of the board of Infosys and the UNICEF Special Representative for Young People and Innovation. In 2018, he founded GAME – the Global Alliance for Mass Entrepreneurship. The idea of mass entrepreneurship is important for emerging economies such as India due to their historical challenges of job creation and unemployment. As Venkatesan points out, tech start ups are "hugely important for the economy but not so important for job creation" due to the fact that they can achieve high valuations by employing few people. "One million turn eighteen every month in India, and in the formal economy large companies have not produced net new jobs, with employment growing at half the rate of population growth."[212]

GAME's mass entrepreneurship initiative targets micro and small-scale businesses due to their significant role job creation. But the problem is that while these businesses form the majority of employment, they are not growing. The goal of GAME, therefore, is to create a new entrepreneurial movement with the aim of creating ten million entrepreneurs by the end of the decade, of which 50% are women, together with the creation of fifty million new jobs. Venkatesan explains his vision of GAME in a systemic and interconnected manner where all four key pillars of Deep Tech—deep thinking, deep impact, deep talent and deep collaboration—are present:

"Entrepreneurship doesn't happen in a vacuum. Entrepreneurship is the result of a very healthy ecosystem. In nature, what is an ecosystem? An ecosystem is essentially a place, a geography where living things—animals, plants, micro-organisms—interact with soil, the landscape and the climate. And then there is this bubble of life—that's the ecosystem. And you have a really beautiful ecosystem like the rainforest because the system is healthy.

It's the same way with entrepreneurship. You need a good combination of what we call seed, soil and climate.

"Seed is essentially the pool of people who want to build businesses; they have the entrepreneurial mindset and some skills. Soil is really important. It's about infrastructure: that place, that city, that town; does it have good physical infrastructure like roads, does it have digital connectivity and access to energy, are there market linkages, is there some access to finance? And finally there is climate, which is about two things. One is how easy it is to start and run a business. How much corruption is there? Is it limited or is it unbearable? And then it's about culture. Culture is already hugely important, we've learnt. If there are already successful entrepreneurs, they become role models, they become mentors. What does the entrepreneurial culture say about risk-taking when a young person wants to start a business? What we have learnt is that unless all these factors come together in a place, you don't get a flourishing of entrepreneurship."[213]

GAME recognises that while there are many excellent initiatives such as creating incubators, training programmes and fund raising for micro-entrepreneurs, a systemic view is needed to bring these initiatives together in an intentional way. Venkatesan does not believe that this has been achieved before, due to the complexity and emergent factors that have resulted in tech centres such as Silicon Valley and Bangalore and financial centres such as London and New York. For this reason, GAME is investigating the dynamics of mass entrepreneurship and contemplating how to break out of these centres which have the potential to become monocultural hubs. While Venkatesan recognises that while the opportunity to create such levels of social impact is "extraordinarily large", he believes that those in the technology and sustainability fields have "not yet applied our minds enough" for challenges and opportunities of such complexity.[214]

One way to reveal the hidden patterns of complexity in our human and technological systems is through the arts. In previous ages, it has been the arts and culture which have shaped the way in which we see and understand ourselves. We now need to ask how technology's impact on the arts is transforming artistic expression, and how the ways in which our own artistry is evolving in relation to how we see ourselves, how we can explore our humanity and how we can find ways for both technology and the arts to evolve.

Our Deep Tech ecosystem is exploring philosophy as a means of designing technology which is better able to produce meaningful impact in the world. By developing our own levels of personal mastery in Deep Tech, while consciously maintaining our individual identities, our aim is not just to develop technical skills but also to create new ways of being and new ways of working together, exploring new types of collective leadership skills which make sense in the context of the digital economy.

The new generation of leaders can be thought of as guardians of collective mastery within their amplified organisations, developing new rituals, a higher quality of culture and understanding the organisation as a living system, as a dynamic whole. This new form of leadership requires an ability to develop not just higher levels of personal mastery in individuals, but also to have an ability to develop the collective mastery across their ecosystems.

The power of any network comes through the quality of its relationships. As guardians of collective mastery, by taking on this new role, leaders will have the ability to open up new worlds to those who are a part of their organisations, and in doing so, through the collective efforts and intelligence of their ecosystems, will be able to use their wisdom to create something extraordinary, opening up new horizons to those they are ultimately serving.

Executive Summary

→ Design thinking is a powerful methodology that can be used to solve complex problems. Design thinking is not one single 'thing'—it is a collection of practices and tools that can be used in different ways to solve different types of problem. The key to success is to ensure that the design thinking process is properly managed and that the right people are involved at all times.

→ A Deep Tech solution is not just about the technology; it is also about the way in which it can be used to develop new ways of seeing. This is what makes it truly profound, rather than highly advanced or complex. We need transformational mental models to open us to new levels of creative thinking. The masterful use of art can help people to do so by taking us into different lived experiences and opening us up to meanings and interpretations previously not familiar to us.

→ The Holonomic Circle is a framework which can be used to explore the quality of an organisation's values, purpose, experiences, communication and soul in all their dimensions. It can be applied in many different contexts, including customer experience design, branding, purposeful leadership, employee experience design, strategy and cultural and digital transformation.

→ Visual Stories is a methodology for the creation of visual narratives that are used to create a holistic view of the organisation and its ecosystem. It is a process developed by Paulo Fabre that incorporates the Holonomic Circle, utilising a canvas to map the meaning of an organisation's purpose, relationships and stories together with universal human values.

→ As we strive to understand what is really going on in our world, we need to ask ourselves "what are the key global forces that are driving change and shaping our world?" Our answer to this question is Deep Tech, a movement which is transforming the way we understand technology and which is shaping our world in ways we have never seen before.

CHAPTER TEN

The Amplified Organisation

THE AMPLIFIED ORGANISATION BLUEPRINT

Amplified organisations are intentional regenerative businesses which are purposeful, engaged and hyperconnected. They achieve meaningful impact through a continual process of elevation, scaling and amplification, by developing technology with soul and transforming through their north star of the New 4Ps. Underlying every word and action are the universal human values, which are lived in every person, articulated through the deep technologies developed and utilised, and expressed in the quality of relationships within the organisation and across the ecosystem, economy, society and environment.

In closing, we wanted to provide a succinct systemic definition of the amplified organisation. The reason is that throughout this book we have been proposing a shift from a mechanistic way of conceiving an organisation, which engenders a fragmented conception and understanding, to one which takes inspiration from living systems theory, which inspires both individuals and enterprises to realise their full potential through the quality of their relationships and their continual ability to evolve in response to changes in their circumstances and environment.

To help us articulate this systemic vision, we created the amplified organisation blueprint (Figure 10.1). While this demonstrates the main elements which constitute an amplified organisation's architecture, it is important to remember that systemic and platform vision comprehends an organisation as far more than its molecular composition. As Brian Goodwin explained, "The parts of an organism—leaves, roots, flowers, limbs, eyes, heart, brain—are not made independently and then assembled, as in a machine, but arise as a result of interactions within the developing organism".[215] The blueprint should be seen as dynamic, focusing leaders on nurturing and improving the quality of relationships, and not just on optimising the parts in a fragmented and non-systemic manner.

We chose to create this blueprint to help leaders and decision-makers facilitate multidisciplinary, interdisciplinary and transdisciplinary forms of teamwork within their organisations and in ecosystem-wide initiatives which cut across organisational boundaries. The blueprint is therefore an invitation for leaders to initiate new dialogues and manage communication and alignment, allowing people to shift their focus from siloed functions and departments to understanding the amplified organisation as an integrated whole.

A new form of empathic dialogue and flowing communication becomes possible through the presence of the universal human values which facilitate transparency, confidence, honesty and more tightly coupled teamwork. In this way, people can start to understand that projects, processes and initiatives succeed not just due to the methodologies which are being followed, but because everyone fully understands the expanded form of consciousness and systemic thinking behind them. For this reason, the blueprint is framed by the universal human values, technology with soul and the New 4Ps.

Amplified organisations exist in states of continual flux, and do not get trapped in methodologies which limit their abilities to evolve and adapt when necessary. For example, certification schemes for scrum masters and agile coaches can be important for helping people acquire the necessary skills and knowledge for agile software development. But being certified should not end up being a straight-jacket which prevents people from adapting and being unable to consider the specific characteristics of an organisation's context. Enterprise-wide agility will not follow though unless an agile mindset is instilled across the whole organisation, including the CEO.

For this reason, we have emphasised the systemic nature of strategy maps and the way in which they incorporate the elevated value proposition. Our Deep Tech

FIGURE 10.1 The Amplified Organisation Blueprint

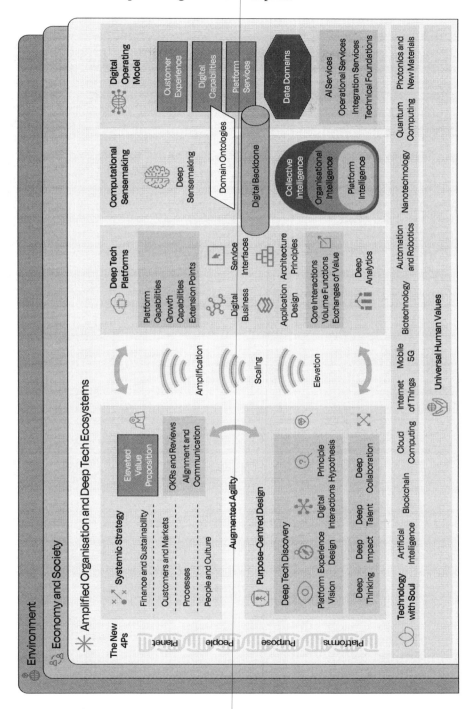

Discovery approach is a way for leaders to start the communication and alignment process, ensuring that the elevated value proposition articulates the strategy and drives developments and innovations in a co-ordinated manner. Aligned OKRs can be set across teams and departments which express the central purpose and vision of the organisation, which is to elevate, scale and amplify their Deep Tech initiatives to achieve impact across their ecosystem, society, economy and environment.

The left-hand side of the blueprint expresses the why of the amplified organisation—its purpose, its elevated value proposition and its vision of the future—articulated in its strategy. These can only be achieved through movement—the elevation, scaling and amplification of the organisation's platforms, digital operating model and computational sensemaking on the right hand side. On this side of the blueprint we see various elements which are present and articulated across multiple digital systems, for example the backbone and domain ontologies. These should not be seen as bounded and discrete systems, but as capabilities which enhance and co-ordinate the technical and cognitive complexity of an amplified organisation's operational capabilities.

Achieving agility can appear to be simple, but it is in fact hard. The reason is that it is not just about mastering methodology, it is about mastering complexity and the unknown. For this reason, there are a number of feedback loops operating in the blueprint which highlight the key areas for organisational learning. An amplified organisation is one that has mastered deep sensemaking, understanding the power of networked intelligence and computational ontologies in order to transform the quality of organisational analysis and decision making. This level of knowledge and wisdom feeds back into the updating of the strategy, Deep Tech Discovery process and OKRs, allowing the organisation to continually adjust to changing circumstances.

The blueprint, therefore, provides a path by which organisations can achieve collective mastery of Deep Tech, understanding it through the amplified conception of deep impact, deep thinking, deep talent and deep collaboration. Economic, social and environmental impact is achieved through purpose-centred design, augmented agility, and products, services, experiences and deep technologies that all express and articulate soul.

THE CALL TO ACTION

Our hope is that our blueprint empowers leaders, decision-makers, entrepreneurs, technologists and designers to start to take those actions necessary to elevate their organisations and amplify their impact in the world. We asked GPT-3 to contribute to this closing discussion by providing some final words:

"In the new age of wisdom, people and organisations will need to have a better understanding of their relationship with technology in order to evolve, to develop and to progress at a more rapid pace. This will require a different way of thinking about technology. This will mean that we have to move from a focus on tools and products to a focus on more open, interactive and participatory systems which allow us to learn and evolve as a species."

GPT-3's insight reminds us that amplified organisations require a new form of leadership where the focus is on the quality of relationships, not just person to person, but team to team, department to department, capability to capability, platform to platform and organisation to organisation. This focus on relationships has significant implications for the ways in which organisations value their human resource departments, requiring HR professionals to instigate their own Deep Tech discovery initiatives in order to transform their employee experiences, training programmes, talent strategies and organisational culture.

HR departments also have a leading role to play in the design, communication and implementation of their organisations' strategies, given that our conception of Deep Tech shifts the emphasis from advanced technologies to a human-centric view of deep impact, deep thinking, deep talent and deep collaboration. Mastery in HR involves helping people to expand their thinking from point-to-point conceptions of relationships—B2B and B2C—to a strategic and networked view of relationships—business ecosystems, experience ecosystems and natural ecosystems.

The opportunity for regeneration through digital ecosystems is immense, with new perspectives opening up new opportunities. Design practices, agile methods and elevated leadership within amplified organisations all require personal and collective mastery to succeed. This level of mastery calls on leaders to be protagonists, avoiding the errors of the past and the blind replication of linear formulas which no longer serve society or our environment. It takes courage to rethink organisations, but this courage and passion to confront challenges can be activated, as Cris dos Prazeres pointed out, through our ability to dream.

When asked to provide a creative contribution to this closing chapter having read our book, a key theme which GPT-3 focused on was 'disruption':

"We need a critical questioning of the societal and ecological impacts of high-tech tools. This time, let's do disruption right. Humanity's greatest achievements have happened when we did not wait".

GPT-3 spoke to us about the need for the governance of digital disruption driven by artificial intelligence, raising a number of pertinent questions:

"In a world increasingly driven by the demand for more private data, AI and machine-learning algorithms, what checks and balances will we put in place to protect people? How can we effectively ensure that private algorithm companies don't abuse or weaponise this technology, while still preparing government, UN agencies and regulators to leverage this data in ways that potentially protect huge swathes of humanity and boost innovation to solve many of our greatest challenges? How do we counter the most extreme voices of inaction, while getting more engaged and collaborating to responsibly leverage digital disruption and AI in innovative ways to solve a growing set of challenges, ranging from climate and energy to global health and poverty?"

The original notion of disruptive innovation described a process whereby small entrepreneurial businesses lacking the scale of resources of large incumbents are able to successfully compete through offering products and services to overlooked low-end customers or new markets. The idea is that they are able to achieve profitability by moving up market, preserving those aspects which led to their success.[216] Following Joseph L. Bower and Clayton M. Christensen's introduction of the concept of disruptive innovation in 1995, other academics and researchers attempted to define the characteristics of this form of innovation, examples being radical functionality, discontinuous technical standards and open and collective ownership models.[217]

The ambiguity of what actually constitutes disruptive innovation has led to the term being misunderstood and misapplied, with people often applying it to any situation in which previously successful incumbents are rendered obsolete. There are also a number of qualities within the term that frame it within a metaphor of aggression, competition and of the devaluation of all that has previously been created. We believe that Deep Tech now provides humanity with the opportunity to change our metaphor. If we can understand the metaphors by which we live, we can better understand how we are constructing reality, and therefore what we accept as truth.

When disruptive innovation ignores the lessons of the past, the same errors are repeated. So we would like to propose a shift from digital *disruption*, which can be destructive and devaluing, to digital *emergence*, which takes a living systems view of digital technology. The aim of digital emergence is to take Deep Tech ecosystems to higher ground, building on all that has gone before, resulting in a new order of organisation based on the quality of systemic relationships. This metaphor encourages us to see the potential in that which currently exists and that we already have all that is needed for the new to emerge.

Amplified organisations, therefore, aim to make the evolutionary leap from digital disruption to digital emergence. Their leadership is characterised by inclusive vision, collective mastery, courage, the embracing of complexity and of facilitating the highest form of collaboration between digital technology and humanity, understanding Deep Tech as the soul of technology.

So our invitation to leaders, designers, technologists, entrepreneurs, investors and agents of change is to collectively change our metaphor. We now have the blueprint available to open up new conversations, dialogues and questions, exploring new pathways of growth, value and impact. Deep Tech calls us to rise to the challenge of the elevation, scaling and amplification of technology to bring the new into being and create transformation that matters. It is this path and journey that will enable people to amplify the internal qualities of their organisations, in order that their value and impact be amplified externally, across ecosystems, society and our planet.

Acknowledgements

The idea and vision of this book began to germinate in 2018 when we first came together to discuss the way in which our Deep Tech series of talks could flourish into something larger that could impact people around the world. As the idea of our book progressed, we launched the Deep Tech Podcast in which we invited many of our colleagues and distinguished guests to explore the multifaceted aspects of our expanded vision and conception of Deep Tech.

For this reason, we would like to acknowledge every member of our Deep Tech ecosystem for their support, contributions and ideas which helped inspire us to bring this book to fruition. We thank Igor Postiga for his artistic and design contributions to bring our vision and concepts alive, Mayhara Nogueira for her research support, and Patricia Arouck and Daniel Vasconcellos for their help and expertise in marketing and communications. We would like to offer a special thank you to Daniela Carvalho for her valued contributions to the development of the Deep Tech Talks and her commitment and support in developing our Deep Tech movement.

We would particularly like to thank Cris dos Prazeres, Aline Fróes and Desirée Queiroz from Vai na Web, Joice Machado, Ricardo Razuk and Ulli Maia from 1STi, Fabro Steibel, Executive Director of Instituto de Tecnologia e Sociedade do Rio, and Yago Dos Santos Cambinda, graduate of Vai na Web, all of whom contributed their thoughts and wisdom to this book.

We would like to offer a very special thank you to those people who have enriched our book through their permission to include their case studies and who augmented our text greatly with their deeply considered answers to our interview questions: Rodrigo Linck and Roberto Del Grande, Pravy; Elifas Andreato and Bento Andreato, Instituto Elifas Andreato; Chris Lawer, UMIO; Ailton Brandão, Diego Aristides and Dr. Felipe Duarte Silva, Hospital Sírio-Libanês; Paula Coussirat and Deny Barbosa, Donatelli; Paula Paron and Maurício Albuquerque, Estúdio Nume; and Paulo Fabre who arranged and co-ordinated the LAB Donatelli case study.

Thank you also to Kimberly Faith, Dave Gray, Josh Lovejoy and Sarah Gibbons for their generosity in permitting us to include quotations and figures which helped us to illustrate a number of different sections of our book.

And finally, we would like to thank and honour the late educator Sri Sathya Sai Baba for creating the Education in Human Values program from which we have learned so much wisdom. We would like to thank and acknowledge Sir Tim Berners-Lee for his vision of the web as a social technology that can unite people, and for his commitment to ensuring that the web will continue to remain open and serve all of humanity, and we thank Swati Chaturvedi for her great inspiration in her coining of the phrase 'Deep Tech' and her work to ensure that our most advanced technologies are purposed consciously, and with values, to solve humanity's greatest challenges.

Notes

1 Matt Anniss, *Instrumental Instruments: The Fairlight,* redbullmusicacademy.com, 11th November 2016

2 Will Brewster, The Fairlight CMI: How two Australians took sampling from their shed to the world stage, mixdownmag.com.au, 6th October 2020

3 *Don't Stand So Close to Me,* wikipedia.org

4 *GPT-3 Powers the Next Generation of Apps,* openai.com, 25th March 2021

5 *Launching the Contract for the Web,* contractfortheweb.org, 23rd November 2019

6 Dylan Lowe, *Check Out These 11 Vintage Apple Ads,* businessinsider.com, 11th October 2011

7 See for example Barley, S.R and Kunda, G. (2006) Gurus, *Hired Guns, and Warm Bodies: Itinerant Experts in a Knowledge Economy,* Princeton University Press

8 *Accelerated Growth Sees Amazon Crowned 2019's BrandZ™ Top 100 Most Valuable Global Brand,* prsnewswire.com, 11th June 2019

9 Dave Chaffey, *Boo.com case study – a classic example of failed ecommerce strategy,* smartinsights.com, 19th June 2014

10 *Ibid.*

11 Andy Carvin, *Tim Berners-Lee: Weaving a Semantic Web, A Sense of Place Network,* alaska.edu, 1st February 2005

12 Tom Goodwin (2018) *Digital Darwinism: Survival of the Fittest in the Age of Business Disruption,* Kogan Page

13 Richard Pallot, *Amazon destroying millions of items of unsold stock in one of its UK warehouses every year, ITV News investigation finds,* itv.com, 22nd June 2021

14 *Ibid.*

15 Carole Cadwalladr and Emma Graham-Harrison, *Revealed: 50 million Facebook profiles harvested for Cambridge Analytica in major data breach,* theguardian.com, 17th March 2018

16 Chris Huhne, *Orwell's 1984 was a warning, not an instruction manual,* fhld.uk, 27th February 2009

17 *Launching the Contract for the Web,* contractfortheweb.org, 23rd November 2019

18 *Ibid.*

19 *Ibid.*

20 Simon Robinson and Maria Moraes Robinson (2017) *Customer Experiences with Soul: A New Era in Design,* Holonomics Publishing

21 Figures retrieved from companiesmarketcap.com, 13th July 2021

22 Peter Fisk, *"Platform" companies now dominate markets, fundamentally disrupting how value is created... time for a business model revolution*, thegeniusworks.com, 2nd June 2019

23 See for example companiesmarketcap.com

24 *Riding the Storm: Billionaires Insights 2020*, UBS and PWC, ubs.com/billionaires

25 *Ibid.*

26 *Digital Economy Report 2019: Value Creation and Capture: Implications for Developing Countries*, unctad.org, 2019

27 *Ibid.*

28 *Ibid.*

29 See for example Juan Enriquez and Steve Gullans (2015) *Evolving Ourselves: How Unnatural Selection is Changing Life on Earth*, Oneworld Publications

30 Simon Robinson, *Brazil's Second Bioeconomics Forum*, transitionconsciousness. org, October 13th, 2013

31 *Ibid.*

32 Werner Baumann, *We need to think bigger*, linkedin.com, 27th September 2020

33 Jef Feeley, Tim Loh and Bloomberg, *Bayer agrees to pay $12 billion in legal settlements, in effort to put Roundup scandal behind it*, fortune.com, 25th June 2020

34 *Breaking through the impossible*, leaps.bayer.com

35 *Ibid.*

36 *Speech given by Mark Carney, Governor of the Bank of England*, European Commission Conference: A global approach to sustainable finance, arabesque.com, 21st March 2019

37 *Biodiversity and Ecosystem Services: A business case for re/insurance*, swissre. com, September 2020

38 Damian Carrington, *Fifth of countries at risk of ecosystem collapse, analysis finds*, theguardian.com, 12th October 2020

39 Swati Chaturvedi, *So What Exactly is 'Deep Technology'?*, linkedin.com 28th July 2015

40 *Ibid.*

41 *What is Deep Tech?*, techworks.org.uk

42 Ingrid Lunden, *What do we mean when we talk about deep tech?*, techcrunch.com, 11th March 2020

43 Megan Molteni, *Now You Can Sequence Your Whole Genome for Just $200*, wired. com, 19th November 2018

44 Josh Lovejoy, *When are we going to start designing AI with purpose?*, medium.com, 20th January 2021

45 Alex Hern, *Twitter founder feels 'complicated' about Donald Trump's tweeting*, theguardian.com, 7th December 2016

46 *Permanent suspension of @realDonaldTrump*, blog.twitter.com, 8th January 2021

47 Mitchell Baker, *We need more than deplatforming*, Mozilla, 8th January 2021

48 *Ibid.*

49 Comment on LinkedIn

50 Simon Robinson and Maria Moraes Robinson (2014) *Holonomics: Business Where People and Planet Matter*, Floris Books

51 Andy Last, *Corporate vs Consumer: Who Owns Purpose In The Organisation?* Sustainable Brands Bangkok, 13th October 2016

52 Simon Robinson and Maria Moraes Robinson (2017) *Customer Experiences with Soul: A New Era in Design*, Holonomics Publishing

53 *What new research reveals about rude workplace emails*, sciencedaily.com, 25th September 2020

54 *Future-Fit Business Benchmark*, the naturalstep.org

55 *A Digitalização da Economia: Inteligência Colaborativa em Rede*, Deep Tech Podcast, deeptech.network, June 2020

56 União Rio, movimentouniaorio.org

57 Elifas Andreato (1996) *Impressions*, Editora Globo

58 *Ibid.*

59 *Base Nacional Comum Curricular: Educação é a Base*, Ministério da Educação, basenacionalcomum.mec.gov.br

60 Elifas Andreato (2017) *Brasil Almanaque de Cultura Popular*, PróAutor

61 Michael C. Jackson (2019) *Critical Systems Thinking and the Management of Complexity*, Wiley

62 Michael C. Jackson, *How We Understand "Complexity" Makes a Difference: Lessons from Critical Systems Thinking and the Covid-19 Pandemic in the UK*, Systems 2020, 8, 52

63 Gareth Morgan (2006) *Images of Organization*, SAGE Publications

64 Simon Robinson and Maria Moraes Robinson (2014) *Holonomics: Business Where People and Planet Matter*, Floris Books

65 *Ibid.*

66 Iain McGilchrist (2010) *The Master and his Emissary: The Divided Brain and the Making of the Modern World*, Yale University Press

67 *RSA Animate: The Divided Brain*, RSA, youtube.com, 21st October 2011

68 Iain McGilchrist, *Iain McGilchrist replies to Stephen Kosslyn and Wayne Miller on the divided brain*, transitionconsciousness.org, Nov 16th, 2013

69 Richard E. Nisbett and Yuri Miyamoto, *The influence of culture: holistic versus analytic perception*, Trends in Cognitive Sciences, Vol.9 No.10 October 2005

70 Robert S. Kaplan and David. P. Norton (1996) *The Balanced Scorecard: Translating Strategy into Action*, Harvard Business Review Press

71 Simon Robinson and Maria Moraes Robinson (2014) *Holonomics: Business Where People and Planet Matter*, Floris Books

72 Maria Moraes Robinson and Simon Robinson, *Holonomic Thinking – Como transformar estratégias e resultados por meio de um novo sistema operacional mental*, Harvard Business Review Brasil, April 2014, HBR Reprint R14004H-P

73 Simon Robinson and Maria Moraes Robinson (2014) *Holonomics: Business Where People and Planet Matter*, Floris Books

74 *Tears for Fears – Mad World / The Story Behind The Song*, Top 2000 a gogo, youtube.com, 8th May 2020

75 *Ibid.*

76 Dave Simpson, *Tears For Fears: how we made Mad World*, The Guardian, 10th December 2013

77 Henri Bortoft (2012) *Taking Appearance Seriously: The Dynamic Way of Seeing in Goethe and European Thought*, Floris Books

78 For an in-depth discussion of this case study see Simon Robinson and Maria Moraes Robinson (2017) *Customer Experiences with Soul: A New Era in Design*, Holonomics Publishing

79 Chris Lawer (2021) *Interactional Creation of Health: Experience ecosystem ontology, task and method*, Umio Books

80 *Hurun Global Rich List 2021*, hurun.net, 2nd March 2021

81 Associated Press and Chris Pleasance, *An extra 200 billionaires were created in China last year as the country's economy outpaced the rest of the world among Covid pandemic*, dailymail.co.uk, 2nd March 2021

82 *Hurun Global Rich List 2021*, Hurun, 2nd March 2021

83 Mark Knickrehm, Bruno Berthon and Paul Daugherty, *Digital Disruption: The Growth Multiplier*, Accenture, oxfordeconomics.com, 2016

84 Michael E. Porter, *How Competitive Forces Shape Strategy*, Harvard Business Review, May 1979 (Vol. 57, No. 2)

85 *Ibid.*

86 *What is digital economy?*, deloitte.com

87 *Email pollution and CO2 emissions*, cleanfox.io, 12th May 2020

88 Emily Safian-Demers, *Digital Sustainability*, wundermanthompson.com, 25 February 2021

89 Design Council, *Our Mission*, designcouncil.org.uk

90 Design Council, *The Double Diamond: A universally accepted depiction of the design process*, designcouncil.org.uk

91 *Ibid.*

92 *Minimum Viable Product (MVP) and Design – Balancing Risk to Gain Reward*, Interaction Design Foundation, interaction-design.org

93 Bill Sharpe (2013) *Three Horizons: The Patterning of Hope*, Triarchy Press

94 Ame Digital, linkedin.com

95 The Future-Fit Benchmark is published by, and available from, the Future-Fit Foundation, futurefitbusiness.org

96 *About Us*, Future-Fit Foundation, futurefitbusiness.org

97 *What You Need to Know*, Future-Fit Foundation, futurefitbusiness.org

98 *Ibid.*

99 Jeanne W. Ross, Ina M. Sebastian, Cynthia M. Beath, Lipsa Jha, and the Technology Advantage Practice of The Boston Consulting Group (2017) *Designing Digital Organizations: Summary of Survey Findings*, MIT Center for Information Systems Research (The research notes that the finding for agility is not statistically significant due to the small sample size.)

100 Simon Robinson, *A Dramatic Visualisation of Terms & Conditions*, medium.com, 17th December 2020

101 *Ibid.*

102 Brian Foote and Hans Rohnert (1999) *Pattern Languages of Program Design 4*, Addison Wesley

103 John Furrier, *Exclusive: The Story of AWS and Andy Jassy's Trillion Dollar Baby*, medium.com, 30th January 2015

104 *What is FinOps*, FinOps.org

105 Matthew Skelton and Manuel Pais (2019) *Team Topologies: Organizing Business and Technology Teams for Fast Flow*, IT Revolution Press

106 *Antitrust: Commission fines Google €4.34 billion for illegal practices regarding Android mobile devices to strengthen dominance of Google's search engine*, European Commission, ec.europa.eu 18th July 2018

107 *Ibid.*

108 Graeme Wearden, *Facebook suffers biggest one-day rout ever as shares tumble 19% – as it happened*, theguardian.com, 26th July 2018

109 Soundcloud email marketing campaign, 18th March 2021

110 *SoundCloud Introduces Fan-Powered Royalties*, soundcloud.com, 2nd March 2021

111 RideFair: An Open-Source Driver Co-Op Ridesharing Platform, kickstarer.com

112 Mike Pieredes and Morgan L. Richman, *The Concept of Good Faith in Commercial Contracts Under English Law*, Morgan Lewis & Bockius LLP, lexology.com, 10th December 2019

113 Atakan Kantarci, *Bias in AI: What it is*, Types & Examples, How & Tools to fix it, aimultiple.com, 13th February 2021

114 Montuori A. (2011) *Systems Approach*. In: Runco M.A, and Pritzker S.R. (eds.) Encyclopedia of Creativity, Second Edition, vol. 2, pp. 414-421 Academic Press

115 Living Species: *Biodiversity*, National Geographic, www.nationalgeographic.org

Animals: Alisa Mala, *Most Populous Animals On Earth*, worldatlas.com, 20th August 2020

Human cells: Eva Bianconi et al., *An estimation of the number of cells in the human body*, Annals of Human Biology, 40:6, 463-471

Viruses: David Pride, *The Viruses Inside You*, Scientific American 323, 6, 46-53 (December 2020)

Trees: Crowther, T., Glick, H., Covey, K. et al. *Mapping tree density at a global scale*, Nature 525, 201–205 (2015)

116 Darrin Qualman, *Unimaginable output: Global production of transistors*, darrinqualman.com, 4th April 2017

117 Peter Grad, *Trillion-transistor chip breaks speed record*, techxplore.com, 26th November 2020

118 *Cerebras Systems: Achieving Industry Best AI Performance Through A Systems Approach*, White Paper 03, cerebras.net

119 *Ibid.*

120 Dr. Ian Cutress, *Cerebras Unveils Wafer Scale Engine Two (WSE2)*: 2.6 trillion Transistors Yield, anandtech.com, 20th April 2021

121 Bob Yirka, *Chinese achieve new milestone with 56 qubit computer*, phys.org, July 12, 2021

122 Measurement taken from internetnetlivestats.com on 3rd July 2021

123 Ben Beaumont-Thomas, *Baby Shark becomes most viewed YouTube video ever, beating Despacito*, theguardian.com, 2nd November 2020

124 Donnella Meadows (2008) *Thinking in Systems: A Primer*, Chelsea Green Publishing

125 *12 Systems of the Body: A Medical Assistant's Guide*, hunterbusinessschool.edu, 4th November 2017

126 F. David Peat (1997) *Infinite Potential: The Life and Times of David Bohm*, Basic Books

127 *Donella (Dana) Meadows - Lecture: Sustainable Systems (Full version)*, Christopher C. Cemper, youtube.com

128 Simon Robinson and Maria Moraes Robinson (2017) *Customer Experiences with Soul: A New Era in Design*, Holonomics Publishing

129 *What Is SAFe®?*, scaledagile.com

130 *Manifesto for Agile Software Development*, agilealliance.org

131 *12 Principles Behind the Agile Manifesto*, agilealliance.org,

132 Simon Robinson and Maria Moraes Robinson (2017) *Customer Experiences with Soul: A New Era in Design*, Holonomics Publishing

133 *ClinicalTrials.gov Background*, ClinicalTrials.gov

134 Eric Evans (2003) *Domain-Driven Design: Tackling Complexity in the Heart of Software*, Addison-Wesley

135 Don Tapscott (1995) *The Digital Economy: Promise and Peril In The Age of Networked Intelligence*, McGraw-Hill Education

136 Don Tapscott, *Four Principles for the Open World*, TEDGlobal 2012, ted.com

137 *Ontologies*, bbc.co.uk

138 The National Center for Biomedical Ontology, ncbo.bioontology.org

139 Svetlana Chuprina, Vassil Alexandrov, and Nia Alexandrov, *Using Ontology*

Engineering Methods to Improve Computer Science and Data Science Skills, Procedia Computer Science, Volume 80, 2016, Pages 1780 – 1790

140 Karl E. Weick (1995) *Sensemaking in Organizations*, Sage.

141 Namvar, Morteza, Cybulski, Jacob L, Phang, Cynthia Su Chen, Ee, Yaw Seng and Tan, Kevin Tee Liang 2018, *Simplifying sensemaking: concept, process, strengths, shortcomings, and ways forward for information systems in contemporary business environments*, Australasian Journal of Information Systems, vol. 22, pp. 1-10

142 Murray Shanahan (2015) *The Technological Singularity*, MIT Press, 2015

143 Stanislaw Ulam, *Tribute to John von Neumann, Bulletin of the American Mathematical Society*. 64, #3, part 2: 5, May 1958

144 Simon Robinson and Maria Moraes Robinson (2014) *Holonomics: Business Where People and Planet Matter*, Floris Books

145 *The Future of Jobs Report 2020*, World Economic Forum, weforum.org, 20th October 2020

146 *Ibid.*

147 *Ibid.*

148 Tichenor, P.A.; Donohue, G.A.; Olien, C.N. (1970) *Mass media flow and differential growth in knowledge*, Public Opinion Quarterly. 34 (2): 159–170

149 Hannes Selhofer and Tobias Hüsing, *The Digital Divide Index - A Measure of Social inequalities in the Adoption of ICT*, Proceedings of the 10th European Conference on Information Systems, Information Systems and the Future of the Digital Economy, ECIS 2002, Gdansk, Poland, June 6-8, 2002

150 *Understanding the Digital Divide*, OECD Publications, oecd.org, 2001

151 *Ibid.*

152 *Digital Economy and Society Index Report 2020 – Human Capital*, European Commission, ec.europa.eu

153 Kimberly Faith (2020) *Your Lion Inside: Discover the Power Within and Live Your Fullest Life*, Advantage

154 *Women in Management (Quick Take)*, catalyst.org, 11th August 2020

155 *Ibid.*

156 *Women in Digital Scoreboard 2020*, The European Commission, ec.europa.eu, 2020

157 *Why Gender Parity Matters*, World Economic Forum, weforum.org, 16th December 2019

158 *Global Gender Gap Report 2020*, World Economic Forum, weforum.org, 16th December 2019

159 Victoria Masterton, *The state of women's leadership in 5 statistics*, weforum.org, 3rd November 2020

160 *Diversity, Equity and Inclusion 4.0 A toolkit for leaders to accelerate social progress in the future of work*, World Economic Forum, weforum.org, June 2020

161 *Ibid.*

162 *Ibid.*

163 *Ibid.*

164 Larry Fink, *Larry Fink's 2021 Letter to CEOs*, blackrock.com, January 2021

165 Nathan Reiff, *How BlackRock Makes Money*, Investopedia.com, 27th February, 2021

166 *Ibid.*

167 *Favela*, wikipedia.org

168 Data Forum Favela, *Data Favela Forum: Racism*, COVID-19 and Inequality in Brazil, UNESCO, unesco.org

169 *List of countries and dependencies by population*, wikipedia.org, retrieved 13th July 2021

170 Instituto Data Favela, research presented at 2° Fórum Nova Favela Brasileira, 2015

171 *Ibid.*

172 *Ibid.*

173 *TIC Domicílios – 2019*, cetic.br

174 Peter C. Evans, *The Race for Platform Talent: Who is Looking and Why?*, linkedin.com, 6th January 2020

175 University of Glasgow, *Trees may work together to form resource-sharing networks with root grafts*, phys.Org, 5th May 2021

176 See for example Anthony Toby O'Geen (2013) *Soil Water Dynamics*, Nature Education Knowledge 4(5):9

177 Michael E. Porter and Mark R. Kramer, *Creating Shared Value: how to reinvent capitalism—and unleash a wave of innovation and growth*, Harvard Business Review, January – February 2001

178 Ed Michaels, Helen Handfield-Jones and Beth Axelrod (2001) *The War for Talent*, Harvard Business Review Press

179 Peter F. Drucker (1993) *Post-Capitalist Society*, HarperCollins

180 *Ibid.*

181 Earth is estimated to be 4.54 billion years old, plus or minus 50 million years. *Age of the Earth*, National Geographic, nationalgeographic.org

182 Dr. Neil deGrasse Tyson (2014) *Cosmos: A SpaceTime Odyssey*, 20th Century Fox

183 Global Footprint Network, *Earth Overshoot Day*, overshootday.org

184 R. Andres Castaneda Aguilar et al., *September 2020 global poverty update from the World Bank: New annual poverty estimates using the revised 2011 PPPs*, World Bank, worldbank.org, 7th October 2020

185 Simon Robinson and Maria Moraes Robinson (2017) *Customer Experiences with Soul: A New Era in Design*, Holonomics Publishing

186 *Apple names Deirdre O'Brien senior vice president of Retail + People*, apple.com, 5th February 2019

187 Dr Kaveh Abhari, *Why meaning is the key to employee experience – and customer*

satisfaction, The Economist Intelligence Unit, theexperienceofwork.economist.com, 2019

188 *The experience of work: The role of technology in productivity and engagement*, The Economist Intelligence Unit, theexperienceofwork.economist.com, 2019

189 Simon Robinson and Maria Moraes Robinson (2014) *Holonomics: Business Where People and Planet Matter*, Floris Books

190 Photos reproduced from Simon Robinson and Maria Moraes Robinson (2014) *Holonomics: Business Where People and Planet Matter*, Floris Books

191 Kazuo Inamori (2012) *Amoeba Management: The Dynamic Management System for Rapid Market Response*, Productivity Press

192 *John Bonner's slime mold movies*, Princeton University, youtube.com, 22nd January 2010

193 Dave Gray, Sunni Brown and James Macanufo (2010) *Gamestorming: A Playbook for Innovators*, Rulebreakers and Changemakers, O'Reilly

194 Dave Gray, *Updated Empathy Map Canvas*, medium.com, 17th July 2017

195 Philip N. Johnson-Laird (2004) *Mental models and reasoning.* In J.P Leighton and R.J. Sternberg (eds.) *The nature of reasoning*, Cambridge University Press

196 Marco Ragni and Marcus Knauff (2013) *A theory and computational model of spatial reasoning with preferred mental models.* Psychological Review, 120: 561-88

197 *Ibid.*

198 Rikke Friis Dam and Teo Yu Siang (2020) *What is Design Thinking and Why Is It So Popular?*, Interaction Design Foundation, interaction-design.org

199 Shane Ketterman, *Exploring the reasons for Design Thinking criticism*, UX Collective, medium.com, 5th June 2009

200 *Redesigners for Justice: the leaders we need for an equitable future*, Creative Reaction Lab, medium.com, 23rd September 2019

201 *Our Theory of Change*, Creative Reaction Lab, creativereactionlab.com

202 *Ibid.*

203 Sarah Gibbons, *Design Thinking 101*, Nielsen Norman Group, nngroup.com, 31st July 2016

204 Variations of this quote have been misattributed to Albert Einstein. The source of the historical quote comes from quoteinvestigator.com: William H. Markle, *The Manufacturing Manager's Skills* in Robert E. Finley and Henry R. Ziobro (1966) *The Manufacturing Man and His Job*, American Management Association, Inc.

205 Mike Atyeo and Simon Robinson (1995) *Delivering Competitive Edge*, in *Human-Computer Interaction: Interact '95 (IFIP Advances in Information and Communication Technology*, Knut Nordby (Editor), Per Helmersen (Editor), David Gilmore (Editor), Springer

206 See for example Jonathan A. Smith, Paulo Flowers and Michael Larkin (2009) *Interpretative Phenomenological Analysis*, Sage

207 Martin Heidegger (1977) *The Question Concerning Technology: And Other Essays*, Harper and Row

208 Simon Robinson and Maria Moraes Robinson (2017) *Customer Experiences with Soul: A New Era in Design*, Holonomics Publishing

209 Paulo Fabre, paulofabre.com.br

210 Donatelli, donatelli.com.br

211 See for example Robert Booth, *Facebook reveals news feed experiment to control emotions*, theguardian.com, 30th June 2014

212 *"Ask an Expert" with Ravi Venkatesan on empowering entrepreneurs to help communities thrive*, IKEA Foundation, youtube.com, 12th November 2020

213 *Ibid.*

214 *Ibid.*

215 Brian Goodwin (1994) *How the Leopard Changed Its Spots*, Phoenix

216 Clayton M. Christensen, Michael E. Raynor and Rory McDonald, *What Is Disruptive Innovation?*, Harvard Business Review, December 2015

217 Joseph Schuessler and Delmer Nagy, *Defining and Predicting Disruptive Innovations*, Conference: 2014 Annual Meeting of Decision Sciences Institute, November 2014, published by Joseph Schuessler on researchgate.net

Index

About the Authors

Simon Robinson

With three decades of experience in customer experience design, Simon is an internet pioneer and award-winning innovator, having co-founded British Telecom's Genie Internet, the world's first mobile internet portal, and contributing to the design and launch of the world's first smart phones. He is the CEO (Worldwide) of Holonomics, co-founder of the Deep Tech Network, a Harvard Business Review author, and coauthor of *Customer Experiences with Soul: A New Era in Design* and *Holonomics: Business Where People and Planet Matter*. Simon is respected globally for his contributions to customer experience strategy and Deep Tech, having created numerous design methods and frameworks such as the New 4Ps and the Holonomic Circle.

Igor Couto

Igor is a visionary technologist and social impact entrepreneur, sought after by the world's largest organisations for his expertise in implementing mission-critical systems and generating transformational impact for national and multinational enterprises in the areas of digital economy, agile organisations, digital architectures, intelligent systems and purpose-centred design. He is the CEO and co-founder of Deep Tech design house 1STi, co-founder of the Deep Tech Network, and co-founder of Vai na Web, the internationally-recognised movement developing deeply talented IT professionals who come from disadvantaged backgrounds.

Maria Moraes Robinson

Maria is an economist and a specialist in strategy and organisational transformation, internationally recognised for her innovation in the fields of digital and cultural transformation, Balanced Scorecard, employee experience, agile strategy, and championing the role of universal human values in Deep Tech. Her contributions to leadership thinking have transformed the way in which business leaders are able to achieve augmented agility through understanding and implementing a systemic form of strategy, through a focus on human values, an expanded form of consciousness and the quality of relationships within organisations and across ecosystems. Maria is CEO (Brasil) of Holonomics, co-founder of the Deep Tech Network, a Harvard Business Review author and coauthor of *Holonomics: Business Where People and Planet Matter*, *Customer Experiences with Soul: A New Era in Design*, *The Strategy Activist* and *Strategy Management: Experiences and Lessons from Brazilian Companies*.

About Our Organisations

Holonomics

holonomics.co

Holonomics is a business consultancy that supports organisations in their transformation processes based on the New 4Ps of Platforms, Purpose, People and Planet. We are specialists in the areas of strategy, customer experience, Deep Tech and cultural and digital transformation.

We partner with leaders to implement high-impact strategy, experience design and organisational transformation by using our deep thinking to generate solutions which draw upon the power and impact of Deep Tech. By developing people's skills and knowledge at the deepest level—the values, ways of seeing, creativity and systems thinking—we enable organisations to elevate their value propositions, scale their technologies and amplify their impact.

1STi

1sti.com.br

1STi is a Deep Tech consultancy that builds mission-critical digital architectures, enabling businesses to generate long-term value and embrace future change—now. We bring a unique, systemic approach alongside deep expertise in designing and developing future-proof technologies and digital strategies to effectively address complex challenges and drive strategic transformation.

1STi's unique approach to helping businesses implement platform-based strategies is based on the New 4Ps: platforms, purpose, people and planet. These pillars align with our Deep Tech practice that emphasises values that are beyond product, price or promotion, leading our clients to a purpose-driven approach that differentiates them and drives long-term success.

The Deep Tech Network

deeptech.network

The Deep Tech Network is a movement born in Brazil with an international reach which is the result of a collaboration between 1STi, Holonomics and Vai na Web, three organisations which have at their heart a singular mission to unite advanced technological innovations with consciousness and human values.

The Deep Tech Network movement was therefore created with the objective of helping organisations to find deep solutions to complex problems, expanding their perceptions of the evolution of technology through developing a greater awareness of its impact on society and our planet.

Holonomics Publishing

holonomics.pub

Holonomics Publishing is the international publishing division of Holonomics. Our mission is to publish books which are inspired by the philosophy of our Holonomics approach to cultural and digital transformation and the five universal human values of peace, truth, love, righteousness and non-violence.

Books by the same Authors

Holonomics: Business Where People and Planet Matter

Businesses around the world are experiencing rapid changes in the economy and society. This book discusses how business leaders and managers can respond to these changes in innovative ways, developing strong cultures, trusting people and by utilising high-quality communication.

Customer Experiences With Soul: A New Era in Design

The guidelines provided in this book apply not only to the design of the experience of customers, but also to the development of products and services, organisational design, branding, communication, leadership and strategy. The book will help you take a radically new approach to customer experience design by integrating your purpose, goals and strategy into your customer experience, implementing human values across your organisation and developing more meaningful long-term relationships with your customers.

Printed in Great Britain
by Amazon